GOD THOUGHTS

WITHDRAWN

1 7 JUN 2022

YORK ST. JOHN
LIBRARY & INFORMATION
SERVICES

Written by
Ian Aveyard

Edited and designed by
David Muir

Cartoons by
Taffy

D0314171

Published by **St John's Extension Studies**
Bramcote, Nottingham NG9 3RL

© St John's Extension Studies 1997
  Reprinted with minor alterations, 2000, 2003, 2006

ISBN 1-900920-04-2

Other than as permitted under the Copyright Act 1956, no part
of this publication may be photocopied, recorded or otherwise
reproduced, stored in a retrieval system or transmitted in any
form by any electronic or mechanical means without the prior
permission of the copyright owner.

Printed in Great Britain by AT Print Services Ltd, Rotherham.

Acknowledgements
St John's Extension Studies gratefully acknowledges permission from the following to
reproduce copyright material:

George Bebawi: for *Interbeing* on page 71
SCM Press: for quotations from *Christianity Rediscovered* on page 73
United Features Syndicate Inc: for the Peanuts cartoon on page 55
University of Birmingham Department of Theology: for material from *The Lord is King!*
  on pages 50-51

CONTENTS

How to use this book

Registering for tutorial support

HOW TO USE THIS BOOK

This workbook is not a 'book' in the conventional sense. It is not *about* theological reflection, it is not *about* how to think as a Christian. It is designed to introduce you to a process to enable you to begin to *do* it. Its aim is not that you should become more knowledgable about theological reflection, but that you should become better at *doing* it.

This affects how you use the workbook. We have tried to design it so that it is accessible and easy to 'get into', so you could dip into it anywhere to get a feel for what this process is all about. That might be right for you – perhaps you need to catch a glimpse of what theological reflection is, so that you can make a sensible decision about whether to engage seriously in it. But such a use of the workbook will not enable you to do theological reflection competently for yourself. For that you need to work systematically through the book.

An integral part of the learning process is the writing of a 'journal'. See pages 8-9 for what this is and how to start writing one. As part of that you will begin writing six reflections – three 'personal' and three 'world' reflections. This begins on pages 40-41, and continues to the end of the workbook. There is usually a 'pencil' in the margin so you can pick these points out more easily. If you want to experience the whole theological reflection process in action, it is very important to see this process through to completion in at least one of each kind of reflection. The process is in five stages: try to keep three of each set of reflections going through into stage 2 or even stage 3, and keep two of each through into stage 3 or even stage 4. You may decide to complete more than one of each kind of reflection, but the process *is* time-consuming and you must be realistic. It is better to complete one reflection than stop short of the end with several.

That will not be easy, and you will need some help. We don't usually find new ways forward in the Christian life in total isolation from others. Certainly the theological reflection process is much more sound, more safe, when done in dialogue with others. But there are many ways to do this, and you need to choose the one that will work best for you:

♦ You could do it **with a friend**, each reflecting on your own lives but meeting to discuss and compare your findings. You will be dealing with personal information some of the time, and a good friend will keep the confidences that are required. They will also support you in the difficult Christian choices that often have to be made in the wake of your 'God thoughts'.

♦ You could **find a 'mentor'** who will help you with your reflections. This will be a mature Christian who knows you well and is willing to help you 'think' as a Christian disciple. See pages 10-11.

♦ You could do it **in a group**, with someone to 'enable' the group process – a kind of 'group mentor'. This might be an existing group or one you set up for this purpose. An existing group is usually better, if everyone in the group wants to do it, because people are likely to know and trust each other. In particular it would work well for a group which has just done a 'Christian basics' or 'Alpha' course, and wants to go on to do others things together. If the group does not have a good basis of trust, then it should split into pairs or trios to work on the reflections, and use plenary time to discuss what is being learnt about the process. Such pairings will need to stay the same throughout the process.

The workbook material can be covered in eight group sessions. Each will relate to a Unit of the workbook, except that Unit 2 should be given two group sessions and no group time be given to Unit 3. Each member should work through the workbook on their own before the meeting – about five hours work per Unit, so you need to space the meetings to give people time to do their 'homework'.

Group sessions will replace much of the work which would be done with the mentor. But resist the temptation to replace the writing work with talking. Writing your reflections down is a vital part of the process. Each member might write only one personal reflection and one world reflection – other members' reflections will provide the necessary variety.

♦ You could **engage a tutor** to help you with the process of theological reflection. See page 13 for some detail about this, and there is a form at the back of the book which will enable you to set this up for yourself. The tutor will be experienced in theological reflection and in helping others with it. They will help you choose a good person to be a local mentor, or help you set up an appropriate group with an 'enabler'. They will also comment on your 'God thoughts' as you write them up, and this will sharpen your Christian thinking skills. If you really want to learn theological reflection, you should consider this option very seriously.

However you complete the workbook, it is not a course to do quickly. It takes time to change your thought patterns. If you attempt to deal with big issues too quickly, your responses will lack depth, and the course will become just an academic exercise. If it is important to you to learn how to think and to act better as a Christian, set time aside over a period of six months or more. Decide what other good things you are *not* going to do (that's the hard bit…). Invest in the quality of your Christian discipleship. God calls us to be 'workers together with Him'. This workbook is important training for that work.

BEING A
REFLECTIVE
CHRISTIAN

CONTENTS

PURPOSE

The purpose of this Unit is to introduce the idea of 'theological reflection', and help you see that you already do something very like it.

THE BIBLE POLKA

This workbook is about having 'God thoughts', or what is often called 'theological reflection'.

You may not recognise either phrase, but it is likely you have done quite a lot of this already.

I wonder if you have experienced any of these situations?

As you were reading the bible something seemed to stand out and you recognised it fitted your situation. The more you thought about it the greater seemed the connections. You took the issue seriously and re-reading what happened in the Bible all those years ago you questioned whether it might give you some clues as to how to act now.

Peter was working as a volunteer with people who were handicapped. He did so out of sympathy for their situation and because over time he had come to value the individuals. He wasn't too sure how his Christian faith fitted in. One person he was helping one day mentioned that he felt left out of life, really on its margins. Peter had been reading that Jesus cared for the outcasts. He began to recognise that his volunteer work was more than he had at first thought. Recognising that he was following his Lord's footsteps gave him new enthusiasm and a deeper motivation.

As you listened to a sermon it felt as if the preacher was speaking directly to you. What was being said fitted your experience. On thinking about it you decided that there was enough truth in the words of the sermon for you to begin to see life differently. From that changed perspective you adapted your way of doing things.

Jane's life fell apart in a big way when she was made redundant. She had recovered from the shock and was trying to get things back on an even keel. She was very aware of God's presence in the situation, but whenever she tried to get back into the sort of job she had had before it didn't work out. There were new opportunities but she didn't want them because she wanted to use her experience. Then she heard an Easter Day sermon in which the preacher pointed out that resurrection wasn't the same as resuscitation. Jane began to see that she was only looking for resuscitation and not resurrection. She began slowly to let go her past and rebuild her life with totally new things.

Something happened in your life which left you with a lot of questions. On thinking about it, it seemed to have connections with a particular bible passage. The passage resonated enough for you to make parallels with it. As you thought more, it was suggested that you tried acting in a way parallel to the scripture. Although unconventional you took this action and the results were good (and surprising).

Maggie had a son who seemed to have gone off the rails and by the age of 28 was work-shy and into drugs. Over the phone from his bedsit he would regularly manipulate her into giving him money. She offered him every possible help to straighten out his life but he would have none of it. Then she re-read the story of the prodigal son and decided that since it was his choice he needed to be left in 'the far country'. Even the money ought to stop until he came to his senses and decided to leave his dissolute lifestyle. She had to summon all her courage to refuse his request when next on the phone – and to then wait for many years for the right outcome.

PARABLES OF LIFE

Jesus' parables show his profound ability to hold together his perceptions about life and his understanding of his Father. He did this not only with creation, the fields, the birds, and the mustard seed, but also in stories of sinful men and women – the prodigal's father, the friend unwillingly woken at midnight and the king with talents to invest. Their clarity and perceptiveness tell of the truth that resided in Jesus.

You are good at analysis of people and situations. You see through the actions of others and their effects. In one situation you could see what the individuals were trying to do and knew it led to trouble. From your understanding of God you were able to guess His way of dealing with it, bringing goodness out of trouble. When He actually sorted it out there was surprise all round, especially amongst those who had created the difficulty.

Michael was well aware that the church council were heading for trouble. Their annual accounts were always accurate but tended to conceal the real difficulties in making ends meet. The problem was that many of the members had their own interests (young people, choir, bells, overseas missions) and made sure that what they wanted was agreed. The reserves were desperately low and reducing. Try as he could there was no way of making the members own up to their self-centredness. Then out of the blue came a bequest, several years worth of income. The real issues then became apparent as the members blatantly tried to persuade the council to use much of it on 'their' pet interest.

Which of these situations 'rang bells' for you?

Try to remember other situations where experience and the scriptures made sense of each other.

You have already done some 'theological reflection'!

You are engaged in community and social concerns and have thought about what Jesus would do there if he was in the situation. What would *he* do, squeezed between falling resources and greater need? Some modern form of feeding the five thousand? Or a modern form of confronting the rich young ruler and asking for a donation?

STARTING OUT

Right at the beginning of this workbook it is important that you recognise what you already know and have experienced about 'God thoughts'.

On the previous pages I invited you to consider situations where experience and the scriptures made sense of each other. In the examples I gave, the experience of the person resonated with the scriptures so that some sort of parallel could be drawn. It does not need to be the *same* as the scripture, just something that *connects* with it.

♦ That situation might have been a long time ago, or may have happened very recently.
♦ Someone else may have who pointed out the connection to you or you might have noticed it yourself.
♦ The life situation may be a simple or a very complex one.

Now think carefully about one such situation in your life and write your thoughts down in just a few words. It may help if I take the example of Peter you read on the previous pages, and suggest what he might have written:

Describe the situation
I was working as a volunteer with handicapped people

What were the most important things in it?
These people felt marginalised

Note which passage of scripture was helpful
Jesus by the pool of Bethesda (John 5)

What was the connection?
Jesus cared for those who felt outcast. When I do so I am following in his footsteps

What happened as a result of your connection between this passage and the situation?
I was able to care for handicapped people with greater enthusiasm

---

LIKE A JOURNEY

We often make connections between unrelated things. I have found that writing this workbook has been like a journey:
☛ as I began there was great anticipation and a little apprehension
☛ as I went along I began to wonder if I had enough resources for the journey – energy and determination
☛ once I relaxed there were lots of interesting things to note along the way
☛ as I began to see the end I wondered if I had chosen the right destination

Now you do the same with your example. If you cannot think of one, try doing the same with the example of Jane from the previous pages.

Describe the situation

What were the most important things in it?

Note which passage of scripture was helpful

What was the connection?

What happened as a result of your connection between this passage and the situation?

In groups too

The same kind of Christian reflection can go on in the context of a *group*. It may be that you have been in a discussion group, house group or prayer group where as a result of your conversation you noted a similar process. Write that down in the same way.

If you cannot think of an example, try using the example of Michael from the previous section. You will need to guess what bible passage might have been appropriate.

Describe the situation

What were the most important things in it?

Note which passage of scripture was helpful

What was the connection?

What happened as a result of the connection between this passage and the situation?

THE SKILFUL CHRISTIAN

Motivation

Imagine for a moment that you have never learnt to drive a car. You are left some money in Great Aunt Agatha's will and decide you would love to be able to have a car. Having settled the matter you start by organising some driving lessons.

Not everyone can master the skill of driving a car. The likelihood of success is dependant on the quality of teaching given by your instructor, your previous experience in learning new skills, and your age. However, the most important factor is the answer to the question '*Why* do you want to learn to drive?'

♦ If the answer is 'My mum would like the occasional day out' then there may not be enough motivation to continue when you have made an utter fool of yourself trying for the twentieth time to execute a three point turn and your instructor is going alternately red and white.

♦ If the answer is 'I could get a better job' then the motivation may be greater.

♦ If you are a young man and the answer is 'It will really pull the girls' then your motivation would be strong!

There is more about 'learning' in the St John's Extension Studies workbook *The Distance Learner* by Sharon Roberts and David Muir. See particularly chapter 1 for more about motivation and learning.

FIT FOR THE PURPOSE

The meaning of Christian vocation and how to respond when God calls
Ian Aveyard, David Muir and others

I want you to think for a moment about why you want to complete a workbook on 'theological reflection'. The following are only suggestions as to your motives:

☐ you thought it sounded interesting
☐ a friend suggested it would be useful
☐ you have been required to do it before further training
☐ you wanted 'something to do'
☐ you hope it will help you to be a more effective disciple of Jesus
☐ you want credits towards a qualification.

As honestly as you can, try to write down what *are* your motives, in the box in the margin.

> **Educational research has shown that motivations that come from within us are likely to give us greater impetus than motivations that come from outside.**

The internal desire to understand drives us to learn much more than someone telling us to do so. When someone in authority asks us to learn we are likely to study just sufficiently to pass the course, and then we promptly forget it all.

Of the motives I suggested, wanting credits and hoping to be a more effective disciple are more likely to lead to success than someone else suggesting or requiring you take this course.

MY MOTIVES
for studying this workbook

1.

2.

3.

4.

5.

If you have been *asked* to take this course then you will find it helpful, even at this early stage, to note all the reasons why it will be positive for you. The more motivation that comes from inside, the more you will be able to stick at it.

> **Which of your motives for taking this course come from *within* you? Use a highlighter on your list on page 6.**

This *self* motivation will help when we arrive at the more demanding parts of the workbook. Other research has proved that internal motivation is crucial when you have to think deeply or creatively about issues in your life.

Learning skills

At school I can remember the satisfaction of mastering woodwork yet the utter frustration of trying to speak French. Thirty years on in life, I can look back to the former with a glow but the latter still sends shudders down my back. These experiences are not just in the past. The feelings about French came back six years ago when I thought about, and even tried, to learn Spanish for a trip to South America. Despite plenty of motivation it was not surprising I made slow progress – enough to haggle for a few souvenirs. On the other hand erecting a wooden greenhouse recently was approached with confidence.

Before you go any further towards theological reflection it would help you to reflect on some of your learning experiences. For most of us they are mixed. Note down what *good* experiences you have had in learning. I am thinking particularly of learning new skills. Skills include knowledge, awareness, personal understanding and our own performance. Playing a game includes them all. We need to know the rules, be aware of others on the field or board, understand our own capabilities and be prepared to get involved. So does moving house, planting a garden, interviewing an applicant for a job.

Think about a new skill you have learnt in recent years.

I learnt to

Information I needed to know

Awareness I needed to develop

Understanding of myself necessary

Performance or behaviour that needed improving or adapting

The easiest parts to learn

The more difficult parts to learn

How I overcame the difficult parts

Your answer may help you to know what you have to concentrate on most when doing this workbook. When trying to think of good learning experiences you have had, you may have remembered a few bad ones as well. The bad ones are not just negative. They can help you to understand your difficulties in learning – and what you can do to minimise them.

Note what bad learning experiences you have had. Do you think they will affect your progress through this workbook? What can you do to minimise their effect?

THE DIARY OF ADRIAN MOLE

Great Aunt Agatha visited today. I cooked her a juicy lamb chop but since I forgot the mint sauce she insisted on buying some and sending it first class mail. Why can't she understand that her 'generosity' will make me even more nervous next time she comes? After an afternoon reminiscing about people she knew before I was born she left, thankfully, soon after four. I did my duty but what a relief when she had gone.

I wonder if you have ever written a diary. Not the sort that tells you your appointments and forthcoming birthdays. I mean the type that records your perceptions of the day.

I have only written a diary once. For three months I had the privilege of travelling to do some research. As well as my research findings I recorded my other observations on a tape recorder and every few weeks wrote them down. Re-reading it years later brings much back to my mind; the sights, sounds, people, and funny incidents. It also charts my discoveries about myself and the emergence of a new self-awareness.

How to begin

Your progress through this workbook depends very much on the writing of a journal. It has many purposes. The primary one is for you to record your learning journey.

What you write will be confidential. There will be no need for it to be seen by anyone else, though we hope that it can serve as an *aide-memoire* for you as you converse with your mentor (see pages 10-11).

The journal will be an important part of learning to think as a Christian – and, I hope, of your Christian life – whilst you work through this book. I suggest you take it seriously enough to purchase a special A4 ringbinder (these pages are A4 size) in which to collect your writing. Being a ringbinder it can also include other things that become special. You might eventually like it to include, perhaps, service sheets from worship when you felt that God was speaking to you, the back of an envelope on which you hurriedly noted a flash of inspiration, a drawing or a photograph. If you treat your journal with the significance it deserves, it will become very special.

What we are experiencing comes out as we write. This does not just include the words and sentences. When I write with a pen or pencil, and not through a machine, it gives evidence of my emotional state. When I'm feeling fine the result is flowing, when upset, wobbly, when angry it goes all over the place! The writing in a journal tells these tales too.

These states of mind are significant. As we look back it will help us if we know in what state we wrote. Although you might be tempted to write onto the word processor there is a significant advantage to pen or pencil.

There will be more specific instructions about the journal later on in the workbook, but for now here is enough to get you started.

Time

Try to give yourself a time each day to write. You may find a specific time e.g. a lunch break, is good for you. Some choose to write just before going to bed so that it serves also as a way of letting go the day's activities and relaxing. Whatever your choice be sure it is one you can stick to.

Focus

The focus of the journal is your 'God thoughts'. So it might include
√ a news item and how you understood it from a Christian viewpoint
√ an unusual happening that seemed to have some bearing on your faith
√ a person you met who caused you to think of your Christian faith
√ something that stood out in your Bible reading
√ a relationship that reminded you of your dependence on God

√ an awareness that something seemed to have a greater significance than at first evident
√ some aspect of the natural world that reminded you of God's presence or power

Content

You should try to record
√ what it was
√ what was significant about it
√ what it communicated to you

It need not be long; just enough to give the bare bones of your thoughts.

Style

Start where you are, not trying to impress others with your erudition, punctuation, or lyrical language.

Sometimes it might be appropriate not to write any prose but a poem or story instead. These are equally valuable, and sometimes more so.

At other times the best indication of your mind might be a pressed flower, a diagram or a picture.

GETTING STARTED

Decide now when each day you are going to write your journal.

Now which day are you going to start?

DIARY EXTRACTS

Here are some examples of entries in a Christian reflection journal:

We went for a walk in the park this evening. The sun was setting and setting the whole sky ablaze with light. The colours went from deep red to the most delicate pale blue with a hint of pink.

I was struck by the gradation of light both in the depth of colour, the tints from red to blue, and also the light to dark.

It caused me to think how little I see the shades of things in the world. I look usually for the extremes; right and wrong, beautiful and ugly, strong and powerless. It seems that it would be good for me to explore nuances of goodness, delight and might.

Today my boss came up to me and said 'That was a really good piece of work last Friday. Well done.' I felt like bursting into tears and had to make a quick exit to avoid it.

She normally never gives praise. When we have done wrong she usually lets us know. It was my reactions that surprised me. I did not know how much I longed for affirmation until she said that.

I wonder if that is how it is with God. I'm so preoccupied with confessing all I have done wrong that I doubt if I could hear it if He said something nice.

The news programme showed yet another battle in a war of liberation in South East Asia. There seems no end to the rottenness of humans to each other. There are further dead, wounded and starving refugees.

Both sides claimed they were on the side of the people but both only seemed to be interested in power. As usual the first casualty of war is truth.

I wonder why God doesn't step in and somehow stop all this warfare. It seems to me that if He cared for the world as much as the bible says then He would do anything to stop the destruction.

SOMEONE TO HELP YOU

When I started to write this workbook several friends said to me 'Writing that is going to be a challenge!' What they meant of course was that they were glad it wasn't them!

Joking apart they knew I would need a measure of God's grace, lots of patience, my mind sharpened, and fingers ready to fly over the keys.

How do *you* rise to a challenge?

♦ Maybe you boldly go where angels...
♦ Or maybe you tell enough people to make them think you are wonderful.
♦ On the other hand you may be the kind of person who tries to forget it, minimise it.
♦ Or perhaps you simply worry everyone *else* with it.

This course is challenging. It is meant to be. But the design of it deliberately helps you to meet the challenge, face it, and rise to it.

1 If you want to rise to this challenge then you first have to face truthfully the *extent* of the task.

2 The second step will be the recognition that this is not one challenge but a *series* of them. They will be spiritual, intellectual and psychological. If you are at all serious then I would expect that you will change.

3 The third is to accept that challenges of this sort bring *pressure*. Pressure is necessary for good learning. We are forced to engage our minds and hearts seriously in the opportunity. We try hard – and find that we *can* break through to new understandings.

In doing all this we need help. We will be wise to acquaint others so that they can support us. Our family, workmates or fellow Christians can enable us only if they know our needs. They are not taking the course and do not know what it entails. A substantial conversation about your hopes and fears may be helpful to them and to you.

To respond best you will also have to care for yourself. We cannot rise to challenges when we are anxious, hungry or tired. We do best when we are alert, untroubled and rested. Whatever achieves this is to be desired. We will need to maintain our good habits of personal care and add to them what is necessary for this particular enterprise.

Who knows you are doing this workbook, and would back you up?

What steps can you take to help yourself complete it?

To gain the maximum benefit from this workbook you will need a special kind of person to help you. This person I have called a 'mentor'.

A mentor is not a tutor. We all know that if a person is going to assess us it will significantly modify our relationship with them. Tutors and students modify their behaviour to take account of the assessment

Helpers come in all shapes and sizes. In your journal write about a person who has helped you in your Christian life. You should include a short description of the qualities that make them a good supporter and an account of something with which they have helped you. (No more than 500 words)

Having written it, identify what sort of person is helpful to you in your pilgrimage.

process to come. The student will never tell 'all', and tutors must remain somewhat detached.

There is a clear division between encouraging and assessing roles. If you do this course for credit, you will also have a tutor. The mentor has the encouragement role, the tutor the assessment task.

Using a mentor

The aim of your mentor is to stand alongside you. A mentor is someone with whom to talk and to explore ideas, and from whom to receive encouragement and guidance.

Your mentor needs to be:

√ a Christian of some maturity
√ someone you respect
√ someone who lives within travelling distance
√ someone with whom you feel comfortable
√ someone who can listen with discernment but without judgementalism
√ someone who has perception about how God acts in people's lives
√ someone who is willing to encourage you even if your story seems unusual
√ someone who can be confidential
√ someone who is prepared to let *you* direct the learning process
√ someone from whom you are prepared to receive both encouragement and criticism
√ someone who has time to give you.

You need to meet with your mentor on a regular basis – say every month for at least six months. On each occasion you should give a verbal report on your progress and then discuss particular things that have come up for you. You might include:

√ how you are getting on with the workbook
√ extracts from your journal or written material
√ questions about how best to proceed

You need to talk over with your mentor what you expect from each other and make an agreement covering how frequently you will meet, for how long, and how confidential you wish it to be. Your mentor will need a copy of this book, so they understand what is required.

A MENTOR AT WORK

Pat had a mentor Sue whom she agreed to see once a fortnight during the course. She hoped to complete the designated seventy-five hours of the course in twenty weeks so they expected to meet for an hour on ten occasions.

At first she shared her hopes about the value the course would be in her work life as a probation officer. She also confided her fears knowing that she had started other correspondence material but had never finished them.

Parts of Pat's journal were very private so they were kept to herself. Other things she could share. Sue was able to recognise early on that Pat was being called to stand far more firmly for her belief in the value of human beings.

When Pat eventually discerned that for herself, Sue was able to encourage her, even when it seemed the whole office was on her back over the issues. There were the occasional panic phone calls for reassurance, but slowly Pat gained confidence in her new stance.

RISING TO THE CHALLENGE

When I was seventeen I was reasonably fit and part of the school athletics team. I enjoyed walking and was booked on a school expedition to the Alps in the summer holidays.

I became ill at Easter, and had a major operation. My condition worsened until at death's door. Just in time there was a response to antibiotics and I began a painfully slow recovery. The hospitalisation lasted six weeks. Coming home I found I could walk no more than across the room before being exhausted. But I was still determined to go on the expedition and had two months to be fit.

The prospect of that trip made me push myself to the limit. Every day I walked until I could walk no more. A month before the departure date the limit was half a mile on the flat. Still my desire to join the others in the mountains kept me striving.

Everything in life was geared to this goal. The walking grew better and I started to deliberately climb the hill near home, and then to do so with a pack on my back. I made just enough fitness to not be a liability to the group and joined them. Carrying my pack like all the others I left the Swiss Youth Hostel and climbed twice the height of Snowdon on the first day. Arriving at the mountain hut I was almost unable to breathe but had made it!

The human story is full of people who have taken on a challenge and put other things to one side to succeed.

♦ Who do you know personally who has done so? If you cannot think of someone, ask around.

♦ What was their reaction on getting there? If you do not know, how about asking them?

♦ Is there evidence to suggest they thought it worthwhile? Most people receive great satisfaction from success. Some ignore the gratification – and find another challenge!

Reflect on a time in life when you had a major challenge. Write in your journal what happened, and what precisely the challenges were. Note whether you were successful or unsuccessful.

What were the major factors that led to success (or failure). From that experience can you guess what it might be helpful to remember in the midst of *this* challenge.

Making space

Doing something new often involves *not* doing something else. What in your life are you going to put aside, in order to complete this course?

Goals worth gaining summon the human spirit to great effort.

SOMEONE TO PLEASE?

God

Too often Christians are put off from responding to challenges because they feel that they may take a wrong turn and God will be angry.

This fear is real and many Christians seem beset by it, but it comes from a misunderstanding of our heavenly Father's attitudes. He knows our need of guidance and is always ready to give it when we ask. He knows our propensity for taking the wrong turnings and consistently forgives and shepherds us back again.

The parable of the talents gives us the clue that, as Jesus understood it, his Father prefers to see us attempt to respond to challenges rather than ignore them on the grounds of safety.

There is another danger that we must not forget. 'God talk' is not the same as Christian devotion. Our desire to know more *about* God is best matched with a longing to know *Him* more. You will help yourself by ensuring that your own devotional life does not suffer as you study.

Yourself

These reflections are based on my understanding of what has happened to others as they have *journeyed*. And we journey in order to arrive.

You might join a flower arranging course in order to meet other budding flower arrangers. Although the class teacher knows that this is the motivation of some and therefore makes provision for a substantial coffee break, the majority of the class do want to be able to arrange flowers better!

This workbook is not an end in itself. It is designed to help you make the correct connections between your life and your faith so that you may have a deeper awareness of what God is doing in His world.

A tutor

The aim of the tutor is to help you pull your Christian reflections together with a greater coherence, and assess how competently you did this.

Many people shy away from assessment, but if done well it provides a more objective view of how clear our Christian thinking is. Our Christian thinking can be interesting, creative, very meaningful for ourselves – but flawed. We need help in seeing the flaws (and the strengths) in our Christian reflections, so that we can think better.

If you need to do this workbook for credit, you will have a tutor appointed. Even if you don't need the credit, it is worth considering asking for a tutor. There are more details of tutoring in the Introduction, and a form for registering at the back of the workbook.

WHERE WE ARE GOING

Which of these aims seems _most_ important to you? And which is _least_ important?

Here is summary of what we are doing in this workbook and how we will achieve it. The workbook will:

1. Help you identify theological reflection
There is a difference between devotional thoughts from the bible and what we are doing in this workbook. It involves real connections with the experience of life, and taking action as a result.

2. Assist you to understand the process
On page 5 you worked through each example by responding to five questions. If done carefully, this is a good pattern to begin with. The pattern is amplified in Units 3-7.

3. Clarify your objectives
It is important that you know why you are doing theological reflection. Your motivation can depend on what you want to _get_ from doing it. The better the motivation the more satisfying the work is likely to be.

4. Organise your task better
If you want the clarity, you will need to be sure at each stage of the process that you have completed it thoroughly and rigorously. Appropriate organisation of your work can help this. By the time you have completed the workbook you will have a checklist of what is involved.

5. Give you greater confidence
Correct organisation of the task helps you be confident that the results are worthwhile, can be shared with others and are capable of bearing the weight of any action you decide to take. Talking with your mentor should help to build confidence.

6. Teach you from the experience of others
Much of the material in this workbook consists of examples of other people's theological reflections. The skill can best be learnt by paying attention to how others have learnt.

7. Warn about the pitfalls
Knowledge is power, and power corrupts. Whether you are learning this skill or anything else, you have to be aware of the temptations that go with it.

8. Give you new tools and better techniques
All skills are better done with the best tools and well tested techniques. I hope to lead you through these without either losing your own natural gifting or getting wrapped up in the method. These tools will be shown in operation in examples, but I also hope you will take the opportunities to use the tools and techniques in the reflection you do yourself.

9. Encourage you to raise your awareness
Much of what happens around us has a theological perspective because God is in it. It will help all parts of your daily life if you are more attuned to this. The examples will show many facets of God's action in His world.

10. Enable you to take action as a result
Authentic Christian belief results in action that is based in our knowledge of God. Learning to take that action is a basic part of your discipleship. You may need courage for yourself and encouragement from others to take the first steps.

Unit 2

OFFSPRING
OF A
THOUGHTFUL
GOD

CONTENTS

PURPOSE

The purpose of this Unit is to look at some of our assumptions about 'Christian thinking'. We then examine how far our attitudes reflect God as He really is.

THOUGHTFUL CONNECTIONS

We all think.
- ◆ We plan a journey.
- ◆ We settle what is for lunch.
- ◆ We choose a new jacket.
- ◆ We look into the sky at night, see myriads of stars and ponder with awe.
- ◆ We hear that a friend has decided to marry and sit down with a blank sheet of paper wondering what to write to her.
- ◆ No doubt you thought quite a lot before deciding to attempt this workbook.

Thinking is part of what makes us human. It is part of how God created us. So when we are thinking, we are taking part in an activity for which God made us. What we think might be *wrong* – like adding three and four and making eight. What we think might be *misguided* – like waking a partner at 3.00am to tell them of a good idea. But whether we use it well or badly, our thinking process is God's gift to us.

If what we are thinking about isn't that simple, then it will involve effort and we may have to leave it and come back to it later. We will probably need to focus our minds,

No doubt you thought quite a lot about whether or not to buy this workbook. Write down all the factors which made up your choice.

rather like solving a problem. We are likely to feel tired when we have finished. We might need to be creative, like writing that letter to a friend. We may have to set aside time and permit no distractions.

Facts and feelings

Thinking starts from information. I had Weetabix for breakfast today because I always do. But you might have had it as a result of being too hungry for only a small piece of toast. Your hungriness was part of the information you used before deciding what to eat. So our thinking is partly fuelled by the facts.

But we do not think only on the basis of facts. Some of the data we use is from our emotions. I might feel lonely and decide to visit a friend. It is likely that into the thinking came questions like 'Will my friend be at home?' or 'Is this a reasonable time of day to visit?' I might feel challenged by a sermon on money and decide to give. Choosing to send a donation would probably involve questions like 'Do I have any money to give away?' or 'What's a reasonable amount to give?'

Good thinking takes account of our feelings as well as the facts.

Other parts of our experience are also involved. We might want to take account of *someone else* who is important to us and that person's decisions might affect ours. They may have chosen to go for a walk at the time when we want to be with them; so we have to think whether to have a cold muddy ramble with them or forego their company.

Uncomfortable facts

As Christians we are called to think about the connections between life and our faith. Sometimes we have the luxury of dealing with the questions in an abstract form – questions like 'How can a loving God allow suffering?' or 'Is abortion allowable?' Most of the time the questions are not abstract. They are specifically related to our lives and the lives of those around us. The time, the people and the places are all real and identifiable.

◆ Why have I broken my leg, stopping me going on the mission planned for next week?
◆ The general election is tomorrow and I have to decide which party and candidate most nearly fits what I think God wants for our country now.
◆ My employer says I have to choose between redundancy and moving 200 miles away where I know no-one.

These questions involve serious thinking on the basis of data from many sources – past experience, church teaching, facts, Christian history, my feelings, others' feelings, the bible, important relationships.

In developing our 'God thoughts' we begin by noting all the data, both what might seem important and what might seem trivial. Often by the time we have finished the process, we have decided that what we *thought* was trivial is, in fact, very important. Conversely what at first seemed important sometimes becomes of little significance.

What often happens in our decision-making is that there is no obvious answer. We find we cannot make a decision by straight logic or by a balancing act between choices.

Making connections

Sometimes the right understanding of the situation comes through a previously unperceived connection. We might hear of a friend also moving to the same town as the offered job. We might discover that having to stay at home and pray for the mission creates a new dimension to our intercession.

> **The key to understanding – and action – is seeing connections we had not previously recognised.**

So it has been with many major breakthroughs in human knowledge. Penicillin, the first antibiotic, came through Alexander Fleming recognising that on the dish contaminated with mould the bacteria had stopped growing. Fleming saw the connection that no-one else had previously recognised and countless human lives have been saved.

We have lots of these connections in our minds already. Some will have been made for us by parents, some by teachers, some by ministers, some by friends. Some will be very accurate, some less so.

If we are to think accurately in the future, we have to identify the connections we have already made and make an assessment of their correctness. They are the foundation stones for our future thinking – we need to be sure they are solid enough.

The rest of Unit 2 will help you discover some of the connections that you have already made.

ACCIDENTS OR CONNECTIONS?

Can you discover what connections led to
❶ the design of a suspension bridge
❷ the writing of Haydn's 'The Creation'
❸ the ascent of Everest
❹ the mass exodus from Ireland in the 1840s

Look in the margin of page 19 for the answers.

Look back over the week and pick out two events which were important to you. For each write down:
• What lead to it? (facts, relationships, emotions)
• What were the consequences?
• Five other things (people, issues, events) that were connected.

Note how important each *connection* was.

BEING HONEST

At the end of Jesus' trial Pilate asked Jesus 'What is Truth?' His question in the turmoil of that night echoes many of our experiences when we are searching for truth and it seems elusive.

At that moment Pilate was faced with serious questions. I suspect he was concerned with the truths behind the trial.

- ◆ What was the reality that underlay the obvious fact that Jesus was in front of him charged with attempted revolution? Why was he really there?
- ◆ Why should a group of people who were more than half hoping for a revolution charge someone else with conspiring towards it? What did they hope to gain?
- ◆ Was this a much deeper political plot hatched to get rid of Pilate himself?
- ◆ How could he get anyone to tell him these things? And would he believe them if they did?

Absolute truth?

All branches of human learning are constantly striving for truth. In the 20th century there have been two areas of knowledge which have put a new light on things:

- ◆ *Research in physics* has revealed that fundamental things like time and distance are relative, and that there are things which by definition one cannot know.
- ◆ *The world of philosophy* has come to the conclusion that all our statements have to be understood in the light of the person doing the talking.

In the church, after several decades of studies in mission, it is now recognised that we each read the bible through different lenses – lenses created by our culture and our upbringing. So it becomes more difficult to say abstractly what is 'The Truth'.

Yet Jesus said, 'I am the Way, the Truth and the Life'. He revealed himself as The Truth. We may not be able to say with absolute conviction, 'This is the whole truth', but we can be sure that God will encourage us nearer to Him and nearer to the Truth. Wherever we find truth to be, we are close to Him. This should reassure us. God wants Christians to think and to look for truth.

Comfort is no guide

Sometimes we will not *want* to discover what is the truth. Anyone who has been in counselling and been faced with the truth about themselves will acknowledge that some of it is good to hear and some of it is quite

> **Even if we discover the truth to be uncomfortable, we are better off holding on to it than we would be if we remained comfortable yet far from the truth –**
>
> **and far from God.**

uncomfortable. It is quite a challenge to hold on to the new truths. We shy away from the things we do not wish to know. Yet it is often at the points where we feel most awkward with the revelations and really don't want to accept the truth that the greatest gains can be made.

We may not want to hear ourselves saying that we are somewhat selfish at home, or that we have modelled our understanding of God on a very distant father figure, but if these things are true, we would be better believing them.

It is out of such honesty with ourselves and others that we can find a better way. We can properly tackle the issues of selfishness. We can look for better images of being 'father'. In this way we come to new understandings of God and His world. As we do so there will be some further growth and maturing.

Facing reality

The primary requirement is that we are honest with ourselves. We might like to see the world as the creators of Superman made it – strong men and weak women, dastardly villains and wonderful heroes – but it isn't really like that. To approach the truth requires that we see the world as it really is and not as how we would like it to be.

We might like to imagine that God rewards good people with long life and happiness and that those who do wrong meet a sticky end. But from as long ago as the time of the writing of Job it has been recognised that He doesn't seem to operate that way all the time. We have to come to terms with what sort of God we believe in. And we have to be prepared to own whatever inadequacies there are in our view of Him.

In the rest of Unit 2 we shall try to discern how we presently perceive the world and how we understand God. For most of what we discover, we will be able give ourselves gold stars. However, it may also reveal some of the distance we have to travel. It might be that the view we have is not one which we are comfortable with and we might need help to adapt it. This is work you can do with your mentor.

One of the debates of the twentieth century has been about the nature of truth in relation to story. Can you think of a story which is full of human wisdom, three dimensional characters and a very credible plot? Then think of something like a party political broadcast that is full of facts but from a highly partisan point of view. Which of the two has the more truth?

ANSWERS
from page 17

❶ the use of tension and balance
❷ Visiting London and hearing Handel's 'Messiah' (He was so deeply moved that he burst into tears and exclaimed 'he is the master of us all')
❸ the availability of bottled oxygen and clothing to cope with extreme cold
❹ a famine from the loss of the potato harvest and parts of the Empire open to migrants

TOO FALLEN TO THINK?

I wonder if you have had one of those major experiences in life which has caused you to ask 'Who am I?' Sometimes having to endure redundancy, loss of a child or partner, or serious illness causes us to wonder about ourselves. For some people it takes a combination of these dreadful losses before they look seriously at who they are.

Even if we have never had to seek answers to question like these, we do have some kind of image of ourselves. I recently had a birthday, and one of the family sent me a card (meant to be humorous) with the message that I was born 'ages and ages and ages ago'. Looking in the mirror later and seeing a few more grey hairs I had reluctantly to admit to myself that I was no longer in the prime of life.

Our image of ourselves covers such things as attractiveness, success, age, cleverness, and fitness. Think about yourself for a few minutes and rate yourself on the following:

attractive	5 4 3 2 1	1 2 3 4 5	ugly
old	5 4 3 2 1	1 2 3 4 5	young
successful	5 4 3 2 1	1 2 3 4 5	unfortunate
unfit	5 4 3 2 1	1 2 3 4 5	fit
clever	5 4 3 2 1	1 2 3 4 5	stupid
small	5 4 3 2 1	1 2 3 4 5	tall
extrovert	5 4 3 2 1	1 2 3 4 5	introvert
poor	5 4 3 2 1	1 2 3 4 5	rich
loyal	5 4 3 2 1	1 2 3 4 5	faithless
hasty	5 4 3 2 1	1 2 3 4 5	patient

THE SHAPE YOU ARE

The person you are has been shaped by many factors. Amongst the elements are:
- your genes
- the family into which you were born
- the circumstances you experienced in your early years
- the risks you took as a teenager
- the choices you have made as an adult

You might like to think about how each of these has shaped your perception of yourself. You may find it helpful to explain your background and its effects to your mentor.

Reality or mirage?

Sometimes our image of ourselves is accurate. Sometimes we are simply imagining what we would really *like* to be. And sometimes we have been so often told that we are worthless that, like Cinderella, we come to believe it.

♦ Look back at the characteristics above and note what you wish you were, checking you have not *over*-rated yourself.

♦ Look yet again and check where you might have *under*-rated yourself. If we are to be honest about ourselves before God and others, it is as important to be positive about our gifts as it is to be humble about them.

My list is only a start. What else is important about you? Be as aware of the good things about you as the things you are a little embarrassed about.

The view from here

Every one of the things we have discovered about ourselves (and the ones we haven't) has an effect on our Christian thinking, whether we are aware of it or not.

For example, the bible has many references to rich and poor people. If we consider ourselves rich then we will tend to see these passages one way, if poor another. What about those of us (the majority) who consider ourselves neither rich nor poor? We will read the passage, taking the side of either the poor or the rich depending upon how we see ourselves that day.

How we read such a passage will determine what we learn from it. If you are usure about whether this is true, try the following three-day exercise:

PREVIEW

In this workbook we are using insights from many facets of life: science, the arts, engineering and politics. These two pages have used psychology and philosophy. In the next pages we shall be thinking about whether it is right for Christians to use these and other branches of human knowledge to help us understand more of God.

Day 1
Remind yourself that you are relatively poor compared with the richest persons in the world. Think of them and their affluence and meditate on the words of Jesus, 'It is easier for a camel to pass through the eye of a needle than for a rich man to enter the kingdom of God.' (Matthew 19:24)

Day 2
Remind yourself that you are relatively rich compared with a refugee who has virtually nothing. Think of them and your wealth, and meditate on the words of Jesus, 'It is easier for a camel to pass through the eye of a needle than for a rich man to enter the kingdom of God.'

Day 3
Reflect on what has been the difference in your reactions on the two previous days.

Thinking – flawed or necessary?

This workbook is about thinking. Some Christians would say that the effects of the Fall are that we are totally degenerate. In consequence our thinking is so flawed that it is utterly unhelpful in matters of faith. Instead we have to rely entirely on what God has had to say in the scriptures and in our Christian history.

Other Christians would say that we are made in the image of God and that our ability to think is one of his most precious gifts. We are therefore to use our brains as much as we are able and to look for answers in the scriptures only when we are stuck ourselves. On that same scale as before, what do *you* think?

We are made in His image, and should use our minds to the full	5 4 3 2 1 1 2 3 4 5	We are totally degenerate, and should be suspicious of all human thinking

Your answer here will effect how you use this workbook. If your answer is well to the right of the scale, you might consider the whole idea of having our own 'God thoughts' a nonsense. If your answer was well to the left, you might not have appropriate reservations about the validity of your answers later on in this course.

It might be that you don't like me polarising the discussion in such a way. If so how would you prefer to understand it?

JUST THE WAY I SEE IT

PERCEPTIONS

How are you experiencing the world at this precise moment? Are you sitting on a hard or an easy chair, at home or perhaps on the bus or a train? Are you at the beginning of the day after a restful night, or are you at the end of a frustrating day at work? How does the world feel? Is it good or bad?

How we see the world affects how we think about God. So it is important to explore how we perceive the world.

Now write out a similarly short (say 100 words) description of your own view of the world. Is there a picture that resonates with it?

Let me introduce to you three of my friends.

Jane understands the world as good. It is God's creation. He has provided it full of beautiful things to see and touch. He has filled it with raw materials for us to use to make living bountiful. There are people who use their ingenuity to be creative, both in science and the arts. There are family and friends to make life a joy and with whom to praise God. Her favourite picture is Constable's 'The Haywain'.

Margaret looks out on the world and sees the results of humanity's fall from grace. By our own actions we have polluted the world and might even cause its destruction. People behave with callous disregard for each other. Increasing knowledge leads to growing godlessness. The arts have a strident humanism at their base. She seeks to protect her family from falling into bad ways. She consistently is drawn to the picture 'The Scream'.

Peter is very aware of God's activity in the world. He gives thanks for every meal and recognises God's touch in the little every day things that happen to him. A word here and a gift there. He also notices the devil's action bringing temptation to him and causing him constantly to do wrong. He feels like a pawn in a cosmic game of chess, and is thankful that by Christ's victory on the cross he is on the side that will eventually win. He loves Salvador Dali's picture of the cross.

All these viewpoints have elements of the truth. It would be wrong to say any of these people had a misperception of the world. Do you recognise anything of yourself in any of these three? If so, would you want to defend that viewpoint – or would you prefer to understand the world differently?

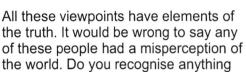

Jane, Margaret and Peter will each see the events of their lives in different ways, coloured by their view of the world. Imagine each had a headache and took a couple of paracetamol to relieve the pain. How might each describe it?

The big picture

We live in a world that God created, is fallen and is redeemable. In writing to the church at Colossae Paul used these words: 'Through Christ God chose to reconcile the whole universe to himself.' It is not just the human beings that are redeemed by God's action in Christ but the whole creation. That includes the whole living world of our planet and its inanimate objects. He also redeems those dimensions of our existence which we cannot see but are nevertheless very real – human realities like power and love, and structural realities like money and politics.

There is a redemption appropriate to
◆ **the world economic order**: The Ford Motor Company, the taxation system, the place where we work, unemployment benefit.
◆ **the world political order**: The government of my country, neighbours as they put the world to rights over the garden fence.
◆ **the world's media and information networks**: The local radio station, what I allow myself and my family to watch on TV.

Taking action – with God

God's redemption of us does not happen without us playing our part. We have to change our attitude to one of faith. In the same way, the redemption of God's world usually needs our part to be played. That requires us to think, speak and act so that God's reconciliation can be brought to bear.

If you think about God's redemption of His world, it may be that you are one of the persons needed to effect the change. This thought is likely to produce different reactions in us depending on how we perceive the world.

Jane would see the possibilities but not the difficulties. She would step 'where angels fear to tread'. She would fail to notice what the forces were that would make the change difficult, and might well try to effect the change with means that were far from those of the kingdom.

Margaret would probably wring her hands in despair saying that nothing could be achieved. She would fail to notice that there were others, maybe not necessarily people of faith, who would assist in trying to change things. She would be so aware of trying to do it without putting a foot wrong that she would not take the risks necessary.

Peter would relish the opportunity to see change effected. He would pray for the devil's hold to be overcome. He would look for signs that God had done it, signs that showed the initiatives God was taking. He would not speak when he should, for fear that he would get in the way of God speaking directly.

> **For most of us, taking action in our lives involves the feelings we imagine of David facing Goliath and Elijah on Mount Carmel.**

You have already written about how you perceive the world. Starting with that statement, write out how you presently play your part in bringing God's redemption to His world, and how your view of the world affects your actions. Suggest a picture or a piece of music that represents it.

GOD AT THE HEART?

Think of one group of people you are involved with and imagine what would happen if the values of God's kingdom (gentleness, forgiveness, truth, peacemaking, openness, judgment, growth) were to be at the heart of things. What would change? You might want to talk about this with your mentor.

BIG DADDY IN THE SKY

Father

Mother

God?

Jesus taught His disciples to call God 'abba', a term appropriate to young children addressing their father. This is the Aramaic word that probably lies behind the Greek at the beginning of the Lord's Prayer, *Our Father*.

Inevitably when we use the word 'Father' our minds and emotions connect with our own human fathers. If our human father modelled and showed the love of our Heavenly Father all the time, then we will have grown up with a perfect image of the father figure. But we know that, however hard they tried, they shared our flawed human nature and have been less than perfect. Those failings and the feelings associated with our human father will inhabit our emotions – and affect our attitude towards God.

If we want to understand ourselves, it will help if we begin by asking questions about our upbringing. We will ask both about how our father succeeded and where he did not. Failings occur not only in ways that are clearly bad – like beating us. Over-indulgence, fuzzy boundaries for right and wrong, and over-protection are also unhelpful to a child.

It might be that you never knew your father. That too will have an major effect on how you feel about fathers, and how you see God.

In what ways did your human father show elements of God's love? And in what ways did he fail? Write in the box in the margin.

I have a friend whose father was often away for protracted periods in her early years. As infants do, she made the connection in her own mind that father was away because she had been naughty. Later as an adult who had a deep faith in God, she still felt that if she did anything wrong God would no longer answer her prayers. Her thinking as a Christian was impeded because nearly all the courses of action she considered involved the risk of getting something wrong, and consequently God dissociating from her.

Mothers too

The feminist movement has encouraged us to think of God not only as Father but also as Mother. The same issues apply – and may be particularly pertinent if you were brought up by a mother only.

In what ways did your human mother show elements of God's love? And in what ways did she fail? Again write in the box in the margin.

An image projected?

You may now have a more accurate understanding of how far your parents mirrored God's love in their relationship with you.

In what respects does your image of a parent differ from what you know about God from the bible? What good and bad effects does this have on your relationship with God?

IMAGES OF PARENTS

Look at the pictures on the following three pages, and see if any of them connect with your feelings about your parents and God. What connects strongly with you on one day may not be what strikes you another, so it is worth coming back to this set of pictures in a few days time.

1. Don't just watch, help me!

2. Not another demand!

3. No fun.

4. Warm and fuzzy feelings.

5. If only I could pray more...

6. Manna is a meagre ration.

7. Why is He so far away?

8. Don't say I've got it wrong again...

If we are to think clearly about God we have to take account of our in-built responses to parent figures. These are different for each of us.

My friend **Adrian** would have identified with the picture of the lady in the armchair. His relationship with his parents was one that made him feel good about himself. Thinking logically was never his strong point so he relied on what felt good when making decisions. When he came to think about issues from a Christian perspective, he automatically tried to find solutions that made him feel good. That really wasn't the best way of understanding things.

BIBLE STUDY

We readily talk of God as Father, and we sometimes think about the image of God as mother. Isaiah 40-65 shows that God is like a good father in that He protects, He forgives, He disciplines. They show us that God is like a good mother because She never forgets her child.

What other elements of good fathers and mothers can you find in these chapters of Isaiah?

THE DIFFERENCE?

Now that you have thought a little about your childhood and your image of God, describe what difference this might make when you think about issues from a Christian point of view.

A GOD WHO GETS INVOLVED

Born, the King of Angels

Christians have consistently puzzled about the nature of the incarnation.

The first disciples who had walked and talked with Jesus were people who, as good Jews, believed there was only one God. Yet they were faced by their strange experience. During His life Jesus seemed to have a very special relationship with God – although so too had the prophets.

The really awkward issues came after the resurrection. They now encountered Jesus entering a room through a wall, ascending from a hill top, sending the Spirit, and speaking on the Damascus Road.

The disciples began their preaching by proclaiming Him 'Messiah'. In his mission to the Gentile community, Paul used titles they would understand, like 'Son of God' and 'Lord'.

Human and divine

It is one thing to say the Jesus is God's Son. It is another to grasp what one means by that. In the first four centuries after the apostolic age, many of the discussions in the church were about this question. Was he just a man with special powers? Was he God come to earth, only looking like a human being?

When they had settled that he was both human and divine, there came a new set of questions. Was his humanness mixed up with his divinity? Was it totally separate? Did one or other side of his nature come at a specific time in his life, like divinity coming at his baptism and leaving before his death?

The church made its definitive declarations at the Council of Chalcedon in 451, though that did not stop the discussion. It still continues, as the publication of *The Myth of God Incarnate* in 1977 shows.

These are not just erudite discussions. There are real practical consequences that flow from them. This particular discussion takes us to the heart of God and the centre of His actions. In loving Him we want, as nearly as possible, to act in His way. His incarnation gives us a pattern for life, for love and for ministry.

Seeing the pattern

The church has taught that in the incarnation we see most fully who God is. In his life, through the attitudes he displayed, the words he spoke and his acts of compassion, Jesus showed what God is like as best as a human being can understand it.

However it not just in Jesus' life that there is much to learn. The whole *process of redemption* in Christ shows the nature of God.

♦ Despite His majesty and power He chose to reveal Himself in powerlessness and poverty, being a refugee at the beginning and sharing criminal status at the end. He wanted to show how open He is to us.

♦ He took the risk of disease, war, famine and failure. He accepted vulnerability in His quest for us.

♦ The cost in heaven of the events of Calvary is beyond telling. All people of compassion are appalled at having to watch a loved one suffer, and His compassion is greater than all of ours. He accepted that cost in order to change our relationship with Him.

♦ The events of the incarnation were ambiguous. No one was pressured into faith or discipleship by being overwhelmed with the evidence. He respects us all.

Most significant is the pattern. He chose to leave all comfort and security and be one of us, accepting the conditions and constraints. From inside the human situation Jesus showed God's love and called people to a life of trust. He was prepared to take the consequences of his action. He still bears the scars of his mission.

In our theological reflection this is one of the patterns we shall consistently meet. It is a pattern we will need to recognise. Authentic Christian thinking and action often mirrors this pattern.

Deviant patterns

But such a pattern is sometimes so costly that we will prefer something less daunting. The tempter provides us with many less demanding alternatives. We therefore need to recognise the pattern's aberrations – deviations which appear similar but are seriously flawed.

♦ One deviation is similar to the heresy called **docetism**. **Docetism** understood Jesus as essentially divine and only *looking like* a human being. Effectively it says God ministered to us from outside the human condition. A modern parallel for ourselves might be when we sense we ought to get involved with something but choose to avoid the heart of the problem. We help, but in such a way that ensures that we ourselves remain untouched by the essential issues.

♦ Another deviation is similar to the heresy called **adoptionism**. This theory was that Jesus was a good man adopted as God's Son at his baptism. In this there is no sense of God coming to share our humanity, but using one of us to save us. Its modern parallel might be when we sense we ought to get involved but instead persuade people in trouble to sort it out themselves. We encourage, but let *them* take the risks.

In authentic Christian thought and action there is not only care for the situation but also a willingness to
♦ carry on in the face of apparent failure
♦ be open to the others' needs
♦ be fully involved
♦ take risks
♦ accept vulnerability
♦ be prepared to pay the price
♦ be changed by the experience

Think of one situation of care in which you have been involved. How far did you really understand the issues and feelings concerned? How far were you changed by the experience?

Can you remember occasions when you tried to care *without* getting involved? What was the result?

WHAT DO YOU MEAN, YOU WANT ME TO **SHOW** YOU HOW TO DO IT ?!

THE SPIRIT OF GENEROSITY

I remember once as a young child being given an Easter egg. It wasn't particularly large, nor in an extravagant box. It was decorated with sweets on the outside and appeared to me to be very attractive – so lovely that I could not bring myself to eat it. It stayed in its box week after week. In time it stayed year after year until it was well beyond the point when I believed it safe to eat. By this time it had lost its glossy sheen, the sweets had fallen off and it was only fit for the dustbin.

It is only slowly and as an adult that I have come to terms with the underlying feelings that provoked this irrationality. I can use now what I have today whether or not I expect there will be anything to replace it.

But I am not the only one whose response to gifts has been foolish.

Hannah feels that she is worthy of far better things in life than she can afford. She somehow expects gifts to make up the shortfall. Whatever she is given there are rarely thanks, and what there are suggest she felt she deserved something better.

How do you respond to gifts? What reactions do you have that are inappropriate, or are not as you would wish?

You may be the sort of person who never expects gifts, who rejoices in the gift and the thoughtfulness of the giver, and who immediately puts the gift into use. Many of us are not quite there.

Jealousy

When Christmas day comes and all the children of a family open their gifts, there can be great disappointments. Michael feels that Penny's present is better, bigger and brighter. Jealousy ensues. The cousins, popping in later in the day, may have much smaller gifts from Michael's parents, but in that climate envy is soon at work.

The Old Testament has the Spirit of God coming upon those of faith – and sometimes of no faith. The enabling may be permanent or temporary. It may be for a work that is clearly 'spiritual' – or for craft or for music.

How we respond to gifts can help us reflect on how we respond to God's gifts to us.

❶ It can help us to discern how we feel about the Spirit's presence in the world. Christians often imagine that the Spirit's activity is constrained within the church and never seen in the world amongst those with no affirmation of faith. In what ways might this resemble Michael's jealousy in the paragraph above?

❷ Paul in the New Testament makes clear that the gifts of the Spirit are distributed as the Spirit wishes and not in accordance with our spiritual maturity. Christians are tempted to make a correlation between their gifts and their own maturity. They also do the same in relation to other people. In what ways might that resemble Michael's view of his parents generosity?

❸ If Michael's mind-set does not significantly alter as he grows up, what effect are these tendencies going to have on his Christian reflections when he is an adult?

Searching for more

As a Christian **Hannah** never felt satisfied with what God had given her. She was always wanting more. That spiritual search was often given full marks by her friends. They were unaware that the search was at the expense of the use she might make of what God had given her. Somehow that never happened very much.

The outpouring of the Spirit, whether in the New Testament or Old, is usually for some significant purpose. Much of it is to facilitate God's mission to His world and to prepare the church for its part in that mission. Christians are constantly tempted to feel that they are never quite prepared enough to fulfil their part in God's mission.

In what ways might this resemble Hannah's life? Given her mind-set, what effect are these tendencies going to make to her reflections as a Christian?

Addicted to giving?

Jesus taught, 'It is more blessed to give than to receive.' But sometimes when we give a gift, we are unsure of what the recipient's response is going to be. Think about the feelings that this kind of giving would evoke in you. My list would begin:

♦ Apprehension

♦ Anticipated rejection

♦ Guilt

Can you add to my list?

♦

♦

♦

God is always giving to us, even though our response is sometimes inappropriate. What does this list tell us about God?

OTHER ASPECTS OF THE SPIRIT

We have thought about the Holy Spirit's *gifts*. *You might try a similar reflection with each of the following words associated with the Holy Spirit.*

**Advocate
Power
Fruit
Inspire**

And what about you?

Now go back to your answer on page 30. What effects might these inappropriate reactions have as you reflect on issues as a Christian today? You might want to talk this over with your mentor.

FROM THE VIEWPOINT OF KNOWLEDGE

In the Western church it was Thomas Aquinas who first convinced people that theology and philosophy should be seen simply as different viewpoints on the world. Before his work in Paris in the 13th century, the prevailing opinion in the Church was that non-Christian philosophy was dangerous and should never be read. Aquinas argued that both branches of knowledge spoke of the same God.

With the growth of human knowledge over the centuries, Christians have often struggled to adapt their view of the world to encompass what they know both from their theology and from these other studies.

☛ Copernicus said that the earth was not the centre of the universe, and that it went round the sun. It took centuries before Christians could accept this.

☛ Darwin propounded the theory of evolution suggesting that animal species change over time adapting to their surroundings. Some Christians continue to be sceptical.

☛ The Theory of Relativity following Einstein's work is probably too inaccessible for many people but may require an equally challenging adaptation of people's understanding of time and the nature of reality.

At certain times in history Christians have effected some major changes as a result of recognising evil practice in the world and being prepared to challenge it. The 19th century social reformers in England had a major impact in such areas as abolishing the slave trade, caring for children, and prison reform. You might like to read about William Wilberforce, Lord Shaftesbury and Elizabeth Fry.

THE
WEALTH
OF
EXPERIENCE

CONTENTS

PURPOSE

The purpose of this Unit is to help you begin
the process of theological reflection, starting
from the end that is most accessible to all of us
– our experience of life.

THE WEB OF UNDERSTANDING

In the last Unit we reviewed the reflections on life and faith we have done previously. I hope you recognise that this is something *you* have done, and probably done all the time you have been a Christian.

In the rest of this workbook you will be taken through this process of theological reflection in greater detail and depth. Some of it will be familiar to you, some less so. The process has five main stages:

- ☛ The starting point, whether experience or faith
- ☛ Identifying the most significant issues
- ☛ Searching for the connections
- ☛ Retelling the story
- ☛ Moving into action

We shall cover these in the next six Units, the first stage taking the next *two* Units.

Reading the examples
At each stage there will be examples of how the process has helped other people. You may find yourself responding naturally 'Well, why couldn't they see that before?' But we all have our blind spots, and they remain dark until challenged in the light of Christ.

We need to keep our minds open to ever deepening insight as time goes along. So in each example the conclusions have a provisionality about them. In a few years the authors might want to change them a little, adding or deleting nuances here and there. So you should not imagine that they are definitive of what *you* should think or do.

There will also be examples of how the process has been developed, both in Britain and elsewhere. Theology is an international enterprise and an ecumenical one, so we will learn from the wider community of faith.

I wonder whether you have watched fascinated as a spider constructs a web. The spider has its own version of 'foundations' as it carefully ensures that each side of the web is well fastened to the surroundings. It spends much time moving backwards and forwards spinning the thread connecting the edges to the centre. Later it creates the filaments that go round the web. These both make the net for the insects to become trapped in and give reinforcement to the whole web.

The process of theological reflection is similar:

- ♦ We will have to make sure the web is well attached – by taking time to analyse the problems carefully or to dig deeper into the inherited treasures of theology.

- ♦ Sometimes we will be making the main connections, with all their creative insight.

- ♦ Later we will be seeking other connections that give strength (and further understanding) to the process.

Starting from either side

Is it better to start the process of 'God thoughts' by asking questions of our experience of life, or by seeking to learn from the inherited treasures of the Christian faith?

Both approaches have their advantages, both their difficulties. In the previous Unit we worked mainly from life, but in the study on the incarnation we worked from the angle of faith.

From life

At first, starting from the issues of life seems easier. The material is to hand. We have only to describe our experience. But because we are immersed in the experience we are not able to be very objective. The culture we come from will constrain our thinking.

Two simple examples might help:

♦ The South American peasant, cultivating a field high in the Andes, might minimise the value of any reflection on her life, as she believes she neither has a voice nor is treated as worthy of a viewpoint.

♦ The British professional teacher, having lost yet another battle in the staff meeting, may come from a background which has taught him to conceal his feelings. If so he may no longer be sufficiently in touch with them to use them to identify the concealed agenda present in the gathering.

> **When we choose to begin our 'God thoughts' from life situations, we need clear and unfettered access to all the appropriate data – facts, feelings, opinions and attitudes.**

From faith

When we start our Christian reflection from the angle of faith, we discover much material that has been superimposed on the scriptures and on Christian history. When we read the bible we do so with the effects of two millennia of traditional interpretation. We may not recognise the cumulative effect of past biblical exegesis, interpretation, sermons, bible studies and school assemblies, but it has all had an effect on us. It makes our fresh insight difficult to hold and value.

For example, the story in the Gospel of Mark about the paralysed man being lowered through the roof has taken on a whole new perspective as a result of new insights from psychology. It is now recognised that some of those who are paralysed in body or mind have a great vested interest in staying disabled, and that this makes deeper sense of Jesus's words of forgiveness. When I explain this insight, there is often utter disbelief that it is appropriate to interpret the scriptures in this way.

> **The more we are well versed in the traditional interpretations of scripture, the more difficult it may be to accept new understandings.**

How to choose

Both starting points are valid, and can be used for different purposes.

Starting from life issues is most helpful when we wish to think about one particular experience and make connections between it and our Christian faith. For example we might want to reflect theologically on a visit we make to another church, or on our daily work, or the trauma of a friend who has lost a child. In these cases we must start from the experience, understanding it in all its dimensions first. Making connections with the faith perspective too early may yield facile results.

We might start from faith issues when looking for the connections between a gospel story and life. Having read the parable of the talents carefully and thoughtfully, we might go through the day anticipating insight as to where it touches the situations we meet. We might notice that a person on the assembly line whose job is mind-numbing, manifests his creativity in the prize onions he grows. However, as in starting from life situations, making the connections too quickly, and perhaps superficially, can result in missing the most valuable insights.

We shall concentrate on starting from life in this Unit and starting from 'faith' in the next.

CONTEXTS

Starting points are often context linked. If you were asked to design a chair your starting point may be dependant on the purpose of your work. If you were asked by a furniture maker to design the most comfortable chair possible then you would probably refine previous patterns. If you were designing it for entry in an art competition then the starting point of an original design might be the first principles of sitting.

What starting point for designing a chair might you use in the context of:
☛ a technology exhibition?
☛ orthopaedic research?
☛ mass furniture production for MFI or IKEA?
☛ a military establishment?

When you have thought about this for a minute or two, look at my ideas in the margin of page 37.

A JOURNAL OF REFLECTION

As you started this workbook you were asked to begin a diary of your reflections. I hope it is going well. Later on in this Unit you will be asked to start writing down some of your personal experiences, to be used as the basis of some structured theological reflection. You may be feeling a bit anxious about it if you are not used to writing your personal thoughts down. Here are some suggestions to help you with this kind of writing.

➔ **Writing need not be prose.** It could be phrases or notes. It can include drawing, symbols, pictures, poetry, dialogue etc. – indeed, anything that helps you put your thoughts and feelings down on paper so you can recall them later. Sometimes these alternatives are more accurate than prose in conveying the realities of a situation.

➔ **Write it as it really is.** When you write it is important to be honest. As Christians we are often prone to fitting life into 'sound theology' without recognising that this can lead to a significant level of dishonesty about how life really is.

➔ **Feelings may be as significant as facts**, and sometimes are more important. You may be a person who naturally never discloses your feelings even to yourself and who has to concentrate to identify them. If so it is very important that you distinguish and record them. On the other hand you may be a person who only records the facts that correspond to the feelings you have. If so it is important that you learn to record all the facts.

➔ **Do it in your own way.** If that means purple paper and green ink written in a tent on the lawn, so be it. To gain the best out of this exercise then it has to be done in the most comfortable way. You need to ask yourself:
- Where will I be least constrained?
- When during the week am I more lucid and animated?
- How can I disclose onto paper things that feel uncomfortable?

➔ **Start anywhere.** If you are like me and can sit looking at a blank sheet of paper for a long time before starting, I encourage you just to start anywhere (even if the beginning seems random) so that the material can begin to flow. It may be that you have lots of ideas of what to write and would naturally start by planning it out. But for these exercises it might be better to launch straight in and see what the results look like.

Why put it down on paper?

Within the next few pages you will be asked to start writing down some experiences that can be used as the workbook continues. They will then be used for personal theological reflection.

You may be asking why we use this method. Writing has some significant effects that are not immediately evident. It will be helpful to you to know about some of these effects and the consequent value of this way of learning.

→ Identifying the important

When we reveal something about ourselves by writing or telling the story, we do not just expose facts or feelings. We also give added meaning to the disclosure by accenting which facts seem important to us at the time. In writing we might underline a sentence. In speaking we may lean forward. But at the time we do not always identify accurately what are the most important feelings or facts.

This is often true in counselling. When someone counsels us properly they are not giving us advice nor encouraging us in the right direction. They are helping us to tell out our story, and to recognise what parts of it we may have overlooked, and what else in it might be important. The parts of the story that we did not at first think were significant turn out to be vital. The counsellor 'holds' our story long enough for us to see this for ourselves.

When we have written something down we can then take a more objective view of it and begin to recognise things to which we were previously blind.

→ Keeping hold of the starting point

Having 'God thoughts' involves interpretation. When we begin to interpret a situation we often lose sight of those aspects of it that do not fit easily. If we are to be skilled in interpreting the story we will have to have constant access to the original uninterpreted story, so that the new ideas can be checked against the facts and feelings of the time. A written record of them is therefore very helpful.

→ Noting the effects of feelings

A full account helps us to appreciate the effects of our feelings on the process. We can note how we sometimes modify the story so that our inappropriate feelings are not challenged. We are also helped to recognise the difficulty of discovering a new appreciation of the situation if our feelings are still strong. For example, if I still feel very angry I will find it more difficult to conclude that the appropriate behaviour is to forgive.

Writing gives us a new window on our connections with our surroundings and allows us to take our feelings into account.

→ Assessing our development

In writing we are able to keep in touch with our development. In re-reading material we can chart our own progress and recognise how far we have travelled. This has a positive effect on the learning process. We can recognise when we are making headway and feel encouraged. We can identify when we are not progressing and then take action to remedy this. We might want to ask for further help, or identify our blockages to that particular piece of learning.

CONFIDENTIAL

What you write in your diary and in these exercises is confidential to you. No one else need see it. You may wish to share some of it with your mentor, but you are in control of that.

You might wish to take some action to prevent family or friends reading or understanding what you have written. People's names can be coded, for example. You may be embarrassed to admit it but it you may feel safer with your material locked away.

ANSWERS

The chairs might be designed:
- ☞ for a technology exhibition, using new technology
- ☞ in orthopaedic research, using knowledge about the prevention of backache and muscle strain
- ☞ for mass furniture production, with a great accent on cost and marketing
- ☞ for a military establishment, seeking high quality, and perhaps durability, portability and safety.

MEET SOME PEOPLE

I have asked three people to share their 'God thoughts' with us at some length. Their stories begin on these pages and continue through the workbook. The stories are not particularly difficult or awkward, though they do touch some of the raw feelings and unpleasant circumstances of life. But the candour with which they are told is rare, and for that we should be grateful.

We start with the part of the stories that is descriptive. You will be asked to do something similar in your own reflections. Each of these descriptions has made an attempt to describe the situation. The issues may seem unclear at this stage but we can expect that later episodes will begin to give the necessary clarity.

DIFFERENCE

Sometimes even basic information must be evaluated very carefully. For example:

- **Age.** We react to events differently at the various stages of life. What may appear an interesting challenge at 25 can be an utterly daunting experience at 50.
- **Work.** Some people have a profession that can be left with a good expectation of return. Many jobs are not like that. Once left there is no prospect of return because automation is closing the labour market.
- **Money.** Many years ago people were brought up to regard debt (except for a mortgage on a house) to be almost shameful. The appearance of student loans has made many in the present generation proud of the size of their overdrafts.

Alison

After a long period away from God, I gradually moved back again into His loving care. In the environment of a caring incumbent and caring friends, I was drawn closer to God and to becoming the person He wanted me to be. As so often happens, God kept showing me areas of my life which were not in keeping with His Kingdom values.

I held a position of authority and power at work, and I enjoyed having a sense of some power. As I felt in control, it became evident to me that I was trying to keep God out of that situation, and I was frightened that if I took God fully into my work place, then my power would diminish, and I would no longer be in control. How would I be able to a tough boss and negotiator if I allowed God to take away my position of power, which was what I felt was being demanded of me?

It soon became evident to me that I could not hold back such an important aspect of my life from His care. However as I began to change, I was at that time being asked to consider taking up another post, based at regional headquarters, on a short term contract to implement a strategy of change. I had previously refused this post, despite knowing that no one else had been asked to do this work, because it meant I would lose much authority and power over a large number of staff. Instead I would have to persuade colleagues and committees that proposed changes were beneficial to the organisation.

Tony (and Jayne)

I was a senior engineer with one of the public utilities that were privatised. Now in my middle fifties I had enjoyed a steady rise through the company over twenty five years. My job was responsible and fulfilling. I worked long hours but not excessively so.

With my wife Jayne I lived in a pleasant commuter village where we were well settled with a pleasant house and large garden full of interesting plants. We had two sons, both of whom were bright. The younger one was doing well with his career and will, one day, probably be a consultant doctor. Our elder son was equally bright but somewhere along the line had become disillusioned. He was in and out of short term work, sometimes living at home and sometimes away.

Both my wife and I had been persons of faith for a long time. I had served the local church as faithfully as I could in administrative capacities and later as a lay preacher.

However for several years we had felt that what I could give to the church was not really wanted. Somehow I felt out of step. It all seemed increasingly difficult. I seriously considered giving up my church responsibilities and retiring to the pews for a few years until certain of what God wanted me to do.

There were other things to consider. Our elder son was making Jayne's life very painful. He was emotionally draining and usually a financial liability. Jayne worked in a volunteer capacity in the local church though her real gifts of home and garden making and hospitality were disregarded.

Sarah

My name is Sarah. I am 48 years old and work in the administration of the local hospital.

I have spent nearly twenty years in a difficult second marriage. Jeremy is a little older than I and has recently retired. I came to faith a few years ago. This, unhappily, only increased the tension at home and I struggled with the knowledge that my husband had openly transferred his affections elsewhere.

Aware of the negative attitude of my husband Jeremy, and not wishing

to challenge his feelings, I limited my church involvement to a Sunday service and one evening Home Group each week. Jeremy said he did not mind this level of commitment.

Our own daughter, and the children from our previous marriages are settled. We have several much loved grandchildren. None of the rest of the family shared my Christian faith.

I also serve as a Magistrate, a demanding and yet fulfilling role. In this I am brought face to face with the realities of human life.

BEGINNING YOUR STORY

I now invite you to write down some simple accounts of significant things in *your* life. The past couple of pages will have shown you some examples of the kind of thing you might write. These are things which you would like to explore later in greater depth and to which you wish to add some Christian thought.

The range of suitable things is enormous. It might be about:
√ a conversation which seemed significant
√ a walk in the park
√ a family issue
√ some pressurised situation at work
√ a friend who rubs you up the wrong way
√ how things are at your church
√ the problem in the football team
√ the state of the house (garden, car or desk)

At this stage you are not looking for any *interpretation* of the situation, nor even any sense of what are the *significant* facets of it. These are best left until later. Noting what is significant and seeking interpretation will be dealt with later in the workbook.

I want you to try to write *three* accounts. Each should be about something different. The more distinct you can make the subjects the better. For instance you might like to choose to have one based on the family, one on work, and one on something in your social life.

It might be that you already have some significant events or people beginning to appear regularly in your journal and which it might be good to use. Look back through your journal and note the recurring people, situations and issues. Note them in the box in the margin.

DO
The aim is that you should describe a situation in such a way that all the significant points are included, in the realms of facts, feelings and attitudes.

√ **Keep it short.** The descriptions you read on pages 38-39 comprise about 300 words each. That is a good length to aim at. Try to write out your descriptions using 300 – 500 words each. (You may not be able to write as compactly and concisely, and your situations may be more complex.)

√ **Give a rounded picture.** If you tend to write tersely you might find yourself having to include information that seems not to be so vital in order to make up 300 words and give a rounded picture. However you might be a person who loves to include all the detail of a story and so you might have to consider choosing what seem the *more* significant features.

√ **Try other means of expression.** I have already mentioned drawing, symbols, pictures, poetry, dialogue etc.

DON'T
Check that you have not included much, if any, of your subconscious *analysis* of the situation. At this stage try to avoid:

✗ definitive and watertight connections between causes and events
✗ certainty about how God is involved and what He wants
✗ imputing unexpressed motives and feelings to others
✗ certainty about the significance of particular parts of the story

Leave these until later. Within the compass of the space, the aim is to make your writing as descriptive of the situation as possible.

It will be better if you are not too adventurous at this stage. There will be plenty of time later for earth-shattering reflections! For now be content to learn the technique of descriptive journalling.

TEMPTATIONS

There are several points in this course where there will be a significant temptation to give up. I guess that now is one of them! For you, attempting this writing may be a daunting prospect. Even to begin it may seem a large step. You are not alone. Even people who are confident about writing often find *this* kind of writing extremely difficult.

1

2 The question 'What shall I write about?' may go round your head many times. This situation is too hard, that problem too trivial, answers to this question seem clear, that issue seems too emotive. Most people at some stage in life are driven almost to a standstill by indecision. We should not be surprised if we find ourselves in this state. In fact, it is a normal part of life for many people.

If you find yourself in this situation why not write about it? You might like to list the issues you considered, and why you decided each was not appropriate. You can then describe the feelings and thoughts you have as you try to make a decision. This is a very positive way to begin one of these reflections.

3 Another temptation is to put the writing on hold until you have read further. Then, you tell yourself, you will be able to do the writing better first time because you will know more of what is wanted. For people who like to have things right the first time, this seems a very positive way to react.

The downside is that, like many processes, one *can* only start the reflection business at the beginning. There is no starting point part way along that will also get to the finish. Every part of the process has to be taken at the right time and in the correct order. (It might be that you started this workbook at the beginning of this Unit without looking at the first two. The material there is very important and likewise needs reading and working through before this Unit.)

So now is the time to decide what you are going to write about, and when you are going to do it. Try to avoid the temptation to go any further before you have completed this task.

SET FREE TO WRITE

George had been brought up with a very domineering mother. At first in life, like most children, he shared his young discoveries and adventures with her. He told her of the time he was so engrossed with talking to Peter that he wandered off the footpath and onto the road. He recounted the story of when he found himself in the shop not having enough money for the sweets he wanted. Slowly he recognised that every time he did so, she would add to the list of warnings. 'Be careful by that road where Peter lives.' 'Remember you have only 50p for sweets.' Worse came when he found that he was being manipulated into staying at home with her. 'The road is dangerous.' 'You haven't enough money.'

George learnt to keep quiet. He would sort everything out without ever mentioning the issues to his mother. When he left home he vowed never to go back except for a day at Christmas. Later in life he found it difficult to ask for help. The underlying fear was that he would be manipulated by whoever he asked. When confronted with writing his real thoughts on paper, he felt it a great struggle. It felt that even the paper would bring pressure to bear. But he persevered with it – and found that the paper did not have power over him. It gave him confidence to share with others, if they did not pressurise him. Gently he came out of his self-imposed prison and was able to be strengthened and enabled by others.

THE BIGGER PICTURE

I remember several years ago leading a discussion group. The members of the group were working towards exercising a leadership ministry in the church. Two of the group were workers in a national utility industry. There came a long national strike. As often there were those who believed it to be right to be on strike and others who thought it wrong. The two found themselves on different sides of this debate. Out of loyalty to their colleagues both felt that they should be taking part in the industrial action. As time progressed the group I was leading heard about the issues, and we also listened to some of the sadder details of the strike.

As I led the weekly conversations I was surprised that many of the group members had yet to address the issues of an industrialised society and a Christian response within it.

- There were those in the group who thought that Christians should never take part in strikes whatever the situation. They cited Paul's views on slavery and authority to back up their views.

- Other members of the group naturally sympathised with the strikers, regardless of the cause of the dispute. They were starting from God's concern for justice for individuals.

- There were those who said they would have felt no loyalty to colleagues because Christians were meant to be salt and light in the world. Christians had a duty to be different whatever the cost.

- There were group members who believed that, just as God was loyal to the human race, so the strikers ought to be loyal to their fellow workers.

- There were those who felt that in the dirty world of industrial and political life, fighting the power of the management and the government with pea-shooters was misguided.

- There were in the group those who believed the only weapons that Christians should use were the spiritual ones of prayer and fasting.

We rapidly concluded that whatever the rights and wrongs of the strike, many of the attitudes displayed in the group were really quite inadequate for dealing with the moral dilemmas the two people were facing. If they were to speak and act on behalf of Christ in that situation then deeper understandings would be needed. No easy answers would be available.

Even well after the strike had finished, conclusions about right and wrong were very difficult to hold with conviction.

Big questions

So far in this Unit we have been considering how to write about situations that are personal to us. This is the best way to begin. However, many of the issues we face are not personal ones but ones in which we are involved by virtue of being members of our community, town or country. We may have little or no influence in the decisions, but that does not prevent us being implicated. Christians are called to think about these situations with just as much clarity. This can be quite disturbing, as we often end up with a sense of guilt at being implicated in decisions we do not applaud and may even believe are wrong.

Thinking about wider issues than our own personal world will require us to think further about our present attitudes. We will have many views on the big questions such as war, capitalism and socialism, the relationship of church to society, punishment, the ends justifying the means. Addressing such topics will show us that we have attitudes which have not yet been thought through carefully. We may find we hold prejudices that we cannot easily justify in a Christian ethos. Theological reflection will challenge these.

We are all faced with situations that are difficult to assess and to make judgements on. That does not excuse us as Christians from having a view. We may start by holding tenaciously to the basic qualities of the Kingdom such as dignity, truth, and faithfulness. From these we will have to proceed to more concrete judgements about the issues and be prepared to discuss our conclusions robustly with those whose views are different.

Some of the questions you might face are:

❶ When is war justified? Is it ever? Does 'peace-making' always degenerate into appeasement?

❷ As a Christian I bow the knee to a higher authority than the State. What are the limits to my own freedom to act in accordance with what I think that higher authority demands, and still claim to be a full and supportive member of the society?

❸ One of the enormous benefits of Christendom is a belief in 'tolerance'. But 'in the name of Christ' are there limits to it? If Christians declare what they believe, should they continue to be tolerant if their views are dismissed?

❹ Christians complain about the treatment of the two-thirds world by the 'West', yet cheered when Eastern European socialism collapsed leaving capitalism not only vindicated but rampant. How far is the faith compatible with a market economy?

WRITING ABOUT WORLD ISSUES

If you want to journal your thoughts and feelings about the bigger social issues, you would be wise to begin with issues which you have some personal knowledge of. This may come through work, or the school governing body you belong to, or the interest you have in a self-help group.

When we have 'God thoughts' about things like these, we need to deal with the starting point in the same way as when we are dealing with personal matters.

☛ We should try to set down the main features of it all without making judgements, avoiding premature decisions about the most significant features, and sidestepping premature interpretations of situation.

☛ Within these main features there will not only be the facts as we understand them but also our feelings.

☛ There will not only be our own perceptions but also those of others on various sides. They too have their feelings which are part of the picture.

All this we have to write down as best we can. We may find that as we do so, some of our underlying perceptions begin to come into our consciousness. These we have to acknowledge also.

BOTTOM LINE?

Adam Smith was a Scottish theologian who wrote about national economics. In recent years his name has been associated with pressure to remove all possible restraint on business. His work is cited as the basis for removing legislation that protects the employee, the consumer and the national interest. People who tend to quote Adam Smith often talk of 'the bottom line' (a reference to profit) as the only thing that matters.

However, much of his writing is based upon moral issues such as justice about freedom and property. He held these moral imperatives were supremely important. This part of his work seems largely ignored.

CONSIDERING THE WIDER WORLD

On these pages are some descriptions of events from the wider world. They will be used later in the workbook and turned into theological reflection.

- The first of these stories concerns a person who was able to have significant effect in the work place.
- The second is about group reflection having an effect in the community.
- The third is also from the work place but on an international stage and in the glare of media attention.

I have retold the stories myself so as to overcome the modesty of the persons involved, although the 'reflections' are those of the people involved.

They are not 'success' stories. The outcomes include much that is good but there is, in each case, much that is not 'success' in worldly terms. There are some apparently good outcomes, some apparently bad outcomes. Both are permeated with truth and the values of the kingdom.

You may not be engaged in anything as momentous as these stories portray. I have chosen them so that you have a sense that nothing is too big to consider, nor too communal.

We live our lives surrounded by situations which are infused with good and evil. It is a mark of growth that we slowly come to recognise these realities in the people, events and communities about us.

Martin's story

Martin was intelligent and personable. He lived in a pleasant suburb in the middle of England with his wife and three children. At the point in his story which we will concentrate on, he is in mid fifties. He had been a Christian for as long as he could remember and had for a decade been a lay preacher. Being a person of integrity he sought to live out this commitment to Christ in his life both in the church, the neighbourhood, the family and at work.

It was the work situation where he was beginning to feel considerable discomfort. He was employed by a well-known national business whose core activity was in heavy engineering. They were also a key supplier for many of the metal-based industries like car manufacture. He had risen through the company to the point where he had a senior role in strategic planning.

Martin's team was required to observe the trends in the business and prepare plans to meet possible changes. If Ford were to build a new car factory what would they do to meet the challenge of the new requirements? If Ford's competitors looked like going out of business, what should Martin's company do to minimise their own losses? Martin was not yet in the position in the business where he had much power except that of influence. He had that because of the respect he had earned over the last twenty years in the company.

The information he was gathering about the trends was not very encouraging. The business may have a near monopoly in this country but imports were beginning to look menacing. They were cheap and soon they would be of similar quality. To remain competitive would bring some big problems. Since labour was cheap elsewhere in the world the future of the business depended on reducing labour costs by becoming more 'high-tech'.

However Martin knew what 'job losses' meant to individuals and communities, and was most perturbed.

The village church story

The church was Victorian. It stood in a field, down a long lane, near the derelict Manor house. Why it might have been built there only a long dead Lord of the Manor might know. Down the dark lane came people from the village. Maybe on a good Sunday there would be forty of them, but on a cold January morning there might be ten. They entered a building colder than the air outside, and draughtier than the churchyard.

The village stood on one corner of a cross-roads. An incessant tide of heavy vehicles pounded by every day, further estranging the church from the people. Most of the parishioners did not live in the village. They lived further up the hill. Only a few years before there had been green fields where the children of the village would go to play. Now there were two thousand houses. The villagers had protested when the council wanted to build these homes. 'Not in our back yard!' they demanded, but lost.

The other newer homes were more acceptable. These were 'nice' people with tidy children, labradors at the heel, and company cars in the drive. They also brought money to the area. Not that they were fully welcome, as was muttered behind closed doors at the cricket club. If they could play they were welcome, if they spent generously in the bar they were valued, but woe betide anyone who was nominated for the committee. That was the province of the locals and only people conceived there could be called local.

The church members knew that hate was wrong. They hoped it was excusable on the day of judgement, since they had been so wronged by the planners who brought all these new residents to the area. But hate it was, and should non-villagers enter the church they would feel it.

A new minister arrived. He felt the tensions. He saw the problems. The difference was that he believed that, instead of the church's remorseless slide into death, there could be some sort of resuscitation.

Paul's story

Paul had wanted to be a soldier since he was knee high. In 1989 he was in the British Army living in Germany. He has done well in his chosen career and was a Sergeant Major with responsibility for over a hundred troops. After 18 years he was an expert in communication – radio, telephones, satellites.

Most members of the armed forces join up looking for adventure – places to visit, good times to have – as well as the more altruistic motives of defending one's country and its values. On the whole they live for the present, wanting to have a good time and enjoying themselves wholeheartedly.

Paul had been a Christian for a long time, coming to faith well before joining up. This faith did not make for any easy time in the forces. The nature of soldiering leads to much aggression. Standing up for oneself is an art to learn. But Paul had to learn not just to stand up for himself but for his Lord and for right, truth and decency. He learnt that if when you stood up for goodness there were others who would back you up – most of the time. These were other times, of course, when you stood up for right and found yourself unsupported and looking a little too pious.

In working out his Christian faith he had chosen to become a Reader in the Church of England (i.e. a Lay Preacher) and had taken the necessary course and passed.

He and his wife Wendy had two children aged 7 and 11.

Prior to enlistment in the Army he had not considered the moral implications of soldiering. In 1989 he had to. In the summer Iraqi forces invaded Kuwait. The United Nations demanded they leave but they sat tight. The other Arab states were fearful that their next move would be to invade Saudi Arabia. Other powerful states, including Britain, were willing to be drawn into the coalition forces that were mustered to defend Saudi Arabia. For Paul this meant the likelihood of being sent to fight. How should he, as a Christian, respond?

ME AND THE WORLD

On pages 38-39 I invited you to write three accounts of something significant in your personal life. Now I want you to do the same with some issues from the wider world.

The past couple of pages have shown you some examples. Write about things that you want to think about further as you progress through this workbook. Choose things you would like to explore in greater depth and about which you would like some Christian insight.

The range of suitable things is enormous. It might be about

♦ an ethical issue that concerns you
♦ a local planning debate
♦ something on the news
♦ the provision of community services or education
♦ a national church issue
♦ moral dilemmas at work (or the lack of them!)
♦ the suffering of a neighbour

As before, at this stage we are not looking for any interpretation of the situation, nor even to distinguish important facts from insignificant ones.

Write three of these accounts, each about something different. The more different you can make them the better. As before, aim for 300 – 500 words each. This is likely to feel more difficult than the previous exercise. It may be that you have never done anything quite like it before.

You will need to remember that the outline will consist of the facts and the perceptions of the different individuals and groups involved. You may discover that there is not even an agreed set of facts.

LISTENING

When people are taught the skills of counselling one of the first requirements is to enable them to reiterate, in their own words, what the client has said remembering both the facts and feelings. In a situation of conflict, understanding enough of the opposition's perceptions and attitudes is onerous – but vital if we are to achieve an outcome in which both parties believe they have been successful.

Next time you are involved in an argument, try it. Attempt to tell the person who disagrees with you what their view is in such a way that they know you understand it. You may need several attempts before they can say 'Yes, that's how I see it.'

In a situation in which you are determined to win, this is even more vital. It was said of Montgomery in the Second World War that he carried everywhere with him a picture of Rommel (the General of the opposing forces). He used it as an aid to knowing the enemy before constructing his strategy and tactics.

Be aware!

♦ There will be facts that you do not really want to include because they do not fit your own prejudices and preconceptions. The temptation to ignore them is very great. Each time you give in to this you will dramatically reduce the value of your work.

♦ This temptation gives a clue to what some of the people involved will have done. One of the tasks of theological reflection is to face all the facts (and eventually to face all the people involved with all the facts even if they prefer to avoid them).

♦ Owning our own views and desires is sometimes difficult. We may expect others to think badly of us 'if they knew', and we live with anticipated guilt and rejection.

♦ This 'owning' is many times worse for those who are politicians, chairmen/women, chief executives, or leaders in any sphere of activity. They are constrained by what will be thought of them (or the group they represent) for even a minor public utterance.

♦ We easily misunderstand others with whom we disagree. In consequence, when we describe their views we, at best, distort them. In a conflict situation we will be wise to expect deliberate and malign misrepresentation.

♦ In these days of 'sound bytes' even those with the soundest arguments in their favour may believe that public opinion is better galvanised by attacking their opposition's reasoning.

THE
INHERITED
TREASURES
OF FAITH

CONTENTS

PURPOSE

The purpose of this Unit is enable you to begin to engage with scripture and the treasures of Christian history and theology, as an essential part of the task of theological reflection.

STARTING FROM HOLY WRIT

In the last Unit we looked at starting our reflections from life situations. Now we turn to thinking about starting from the angle of faith, and in particular from the bible. We shall look at other starting points later on in the workbook.

It is likely that you have done some of this already even if at first you are not able to recognise it.

Whatever your spiritual background you will have heard plenty of sermons that start from the biblical text and move towards an application in life. You may have been in a bible study group that used the same process. You might be able to contrast this with some one dimensional sermons and studies that seemed to have no connection with your own experience, going no further than proclaiming truths with which no-one could disagree.

In your own devotional life you may have done the same. You may have found that the text resonated with your life situation, and from it will have understood God in new ways. You will have similarly had new understandings of yourselves or the world. You may have had the opportunity to try out this new way of perceiving, by behaving differently yourself or by expecting God's action to be different to what you previously expected.

Anchored in the faith

The process of moving from the bible to life has been the traditional way of thinking Christianity.

♦ It has the great value of anchoring us firmly in the faith. We all need a stability that is centred in God's love and faithfulness.

♦ It also helps to prevent us viewing everything subjectively. There are objective truths about God and His world that we need to hang on to at all times.

♦ It enables us to look beyond human resources and methods and shows us that God's intervention and action are necessary.

If you have had experience of a spirituality that seeks to hear God speak, you may have found that as you study the bible devotionally, God regularly highlights words or phrases from it. These may give His guidance, support or encouragement. They may give specific help in particular circumstances when human perspectives seem insufficient.

CONNECTIONS

Most of us read the Bible in small sections. There are readings in church of ten to twenty verses. In the time for our own devotional study we might read a whole chapter. There is much to be said for sometimes reading much more at a sitting. A gospel can be read in two to three hours.

As we do so, whole new meanings appear. We recognise that the juxtaposition of material is significant.

☛ The lakeside scene in John 21 when Jesus asks Peter three times 'Do you love me?' is given meaning by the three times Peter denied him.

☛ Jesus affirmed that James and John would be baptised with the same baptism as his, but it was not his to grant that they could sit on his right and left. Mark later records the otherwise very incidental information that the thieves were crucified on Jesus's left and right (Mark 10:35-40 and 15:27).

It can be very exciting when we discover a new way of being or acting from the pages of Scripture. However it is likely that we also have some experience of getting this wrong. We might have expected God's action in one way and found He acted in another. We might believe He took no action because we looked for it in the wrong place – and missed it. We may have tried out the preachers' recipe, and found the result unpalatable at best and poisonous at worst.

Moored to Bible experience

There are great biblical themes which constantly resonate with the human condition, and which give us insight, encouragement and reassurance in our Christian discipleship. You may have found some of these useful in making sense of the big issues of life:

Abraham's call

For some people (and some communities and institutions) there is a call to leave the past place of security. In departing there is a sense of cutting loose from all that has been held dear. In looking forward there is no certain destination. All one can do is to trust God with the grieving for the past, provision for the journey, and for guidance about the direction and destination. All of this is within the context of human weakness, indecision and impatience.

The Exodus

For some people (and some communities and institutions) there is an invitation to leave a situation of slavery. Unknowingly the bondage has prevented meaningful service of God. As the journey begins there is fear of the unknown. Soon there is a point of no return, and beyond it there are constant temptations to hark back to the 'good old days' forgetting the lack of freedom that characterised those days. There is a new way of living to be learnt and a new trust to be experienced. Eventually there is a new land to conquer, though even this phase is not without its own terrors.

The lonely prophet

The call of God to speak His truth comes to a person who may have no spiritual (or social, academic or intellectual) credentials. Despite great fear and against all worldly wisdom, the prophet takes centre stage and challenges the authorities to return to godly ways of worship and ethics. He is successful in the challenge but the struggle is too great for him. He has to go into the wilderness to recover and to hear God afresh.

Jesus – death and resurrection

Having opposed the powers of evil by truth and the power of God, Jesus went to the capital for the final confrontation. The powers of religious conservatism, personal ambition and ruthless empire-building combined to execute the innocent man. God in His mercy and justice brought resurrection and with it vindication of what Jesus had said and done. In the light of his sacrifice others carried on his mission.

Paul's journey to the Gentiles

Having grown up in a conservative religious tradition he was dramatically converted. After years in the wilderness reworking his perception of God, he was challenged to take the good news outside previous confines. He was opposed by those who wanted to domesticate the mission, but by argument and God's revelation he convinced others of new truth and opened new doors through which many others travelled. Eventually the opposing powers silenced him but by then the mission was unstoppable.

These broad themes of the bible are ones we shall consistently come back to in our 'God thoughts'.

We might add other Old Testament themes such as

- Creation (Gen 1-2)
- The dangers of trying to worship Baal *and* the Lord (1 & 2 Kings)
- The return from exile (Nehemiah and Ezra)
- Honouring God in secular as well as sacred matters (Proverbs and other 'wisdom' literature)

Try to write out similar potted versions of these four themes. You will note that I have removed most of the names and detail so that it can more easily be read with another frame of reference. Aim for about 100 words each.

HEARING SCRIPTURE WHOLE

For further information on the drama on these pages, contact the Department of Theology at the University of Birmingham.

We can try to discover more from the text by meditating upon even the smallest part. For instance, you could try one week to go through the first sentence of the Lord's Prayer concentrating on one word at a time.

Day One	Our
Day Two	Father
Day Three	In Heaven
Day Four	Hallowed
Day Five	Be
Day Six	Your name

When we begin our theological reflection from the bible it is most important that we engage with the actual text. You may think this is obvious and I suppose it is. But long years of experience in opening up the scriptures to students have taught me that although simply reading the text is obvious, it is very hard to do. You have come to the bible with preconceptions about the scriptures based on the theological viewpoints of those who have taught you. These not only colour what we read but also seem to predispose us in what we actually see on the page.

When the text is read by a group of people who are from very different backgrounds then they cause each other to note what is *there*. But when the people are of the same background, then often the whole group fails to read the actual text, or sometimes reads what is *not* there.

Whether we have been Christians many years or only a few months we all need to find ways in which we can approach the bible better. In the following pages are some good ideas. Some you will find useful; others less so.

One way to 'hear Scripture whole' is to expand the text so that it includes the context of the writing. In reading the bible across many centuries and several cultural shifts, we have lost easy access to the humour, pathos, ghastliness, awesomeness, and sensuality included in the text.

With colleagues at Birmingham University John Eaton and Frances Young have written some Old Testament narratives. They have taken the texts and filled them out with historical and contextual ideas. This one is based on the book of Psalms. Walter Hollenweger has done something similar with New Testament passages.

The Lord is King! Moments from the Old Testament's Autumn Festival

Scene One: Travelling to God

Michael
See, brother, how the rains pour down! I can't go into the fields today. Shall I stay and tell you about the festival? I was so sorry you could not come with us.

Jonathan
Please do! Perhaps God will answer the prayer you made for me and strengthen my legs, and I will walk and one year make the pilgrimage myself. But now I must be patient. So tell me everything, and I will see the Lord's glory in my heart.

Michael
Well, as you know, autumn had come and we were growing anxious for the rains to start and break the long drought of summer. But we lucky ones, who were to keep the festival in Jerusalem felt hopes rising as we thought how we would be able to beseech the Lord in his holy temple. He would be coming with power among us to renew the life of his people and all the world. A runner announced the season.

It was so exciting when the leader of our party gathered us for the journey, calling, 'To the house of the Lord! To the house of the Lord we go!' (Ps 122:1)

Jonathan
The night before you set off, I remember, we all joined you in singing hymns and offering the journey to God. I envied you when you set off at first light, with a pipe to lead your songs. Did the journey seem long? (Is 30:29)

Michael
It was certainly hot and dusty crossing the hills! But then we caught our first sight of Jerusalem, – 'Jerusalem built as a city that is at unity in itself' – just the place for all the branches of the Lord's people to meet and be one in praising his name. We came on to the hills that circle the city like the Lord's own arms and we added our tents and huts of branches the orderly rows. We greeted old friends, – and new ones too, for we all gathered as brothers and sisters. Soon we joined the throngs making the first visit to the temple courts. We felt like thirsty travellers reaching a spring, or like birds finding a perfect place to rest so we sang: (Ps 122:3f, Ps 125:2, Ps 84:1f)

Chorus A/B

A: How lovely are your dwellings, O Lord of Hosts!
B: My soul wilted and pined for the courts of the Lord.
A: My heart and all my body cried out for the living God.
B: But now the sparrow has found a house and the swallow a nest for her young,
A: Even your altars, O Lord of Hosts, my King and My God.
B: Happy are those who live in your house, praising you continually!
A: Happy those who draw strength from you
B: Because the pilgrim's way is built in their heart!

Scene Two: Repentance and Cleansing

Jonathan

So you were safely there! Now you must tell me what happened every day.

Michael

It's hard to remember everything in order now. But let me tell you the things I recall best, even if I get them rather mixed up. You know we were one of the parties to arrive earliest and stay the longest, and we were in time for the day of repentance and cleansing. In the great open court surrounding the temple stands the main altar, and there we gathered, fasting and praying though the night. High on the walls, priests were posted to watch for the sunrise and give the signal for the morning sacrifice. A leader sang for us all: (Ps 130)

Chorus A/B

A: Out of the depths I call to you, O Lord! Lord hear my voice!
B: If you store up our misdeeds, Lord, who shall stand?
A: But with you is forgiveness, so that we can worship you.
B: I wait for the Lord, I wait with all my soul, and for his word I hope.
A: My soul looks for the Lord more than watchmen for the sunrise, more that watchmen for the sunrise.
B: O Israel, hope in the Lord!
A: For the Lord keeps his promise, and with him is great redemption,
B: And he, and no other, will redeem Israel from all his sins.

Michael

When daybreak was signalled, there were sacrifices to atone for our sins. And later a goat was sent away into the wilderness, – the scape goat. (Lev 16)

Jonathan

Carrying away all the sins of the people?

Michael

Yes, – but singers and prophets taught us that God wants our repentance above all. One prophet was especially critical:

Prophet

What is the abundance of your sacrifices to me? says the Lord. I have had my fill of whole-offerings of rams and the fat of prime beasts. Wash and be cleansed! Put away the evil of your doings from before my eyes! (Is 1:11 & 16f)

Michael

The king's psalm taught the same lesson, as he sang for us all, confessing sin and asking for God to make us a new heart and spirit: (Ps 51:1,10,16f)

King

Have mercy on me , O God, according to your fidelity,
According to your great compassion, wipe away my sins!
Your pleasure is not in sacrifice, whatever I give; not in burnt offerings do you delight.
The sacrifice pleasing to God is the contrite spirit, a broken and humbled heart, O God, you do not scorn.

Michael

There were songs we all joined in, sometimes very sorrowful, and sometimes rising to gladness. We could not buy God's forgiveness, but the ceremonies of atonement filled us with hope of what God could make of us.

All

Our Father our King Have mercy and answer us
Our Father our King Have mercy and answer us
For we have no power of ourselves.
O work among us your faithfulness and truth
O work among us your faithfulness and truth and save us
Make clean our hearts Make clean our hearts
Make clean our hearts to serve you in truth.

Now read again one of your favourite passages of scripture. Imagine the writer. Who is he? Where is he? What is he writing this for? Did he mean the same with his words as you?

In the text can you discover anything that might be lost in a twentieth century reading of it (e.g. humour, pathos, awe, sensuality, sarcasm, innuendo)?

INTERVIEWING THE TEXT

A key part of most TV news programmes is an interview with one of the participants in an important news story. This may be a politician or an expert of some kind, or it may be a very ordinary person caught up in significant events. The aim is to get 'inside' the story, to see what the real issues are or to understand the 'human angle' better.

Usually there is a line of enquiry starting with some prepared questions, often agreed beforehand. The interviewer is looking for answers to the questions he or she thinks are important – even if the interviewee sometimes has other ideas! The interviewer also has the discretion to use his or her own intuition to follow up a previous answer with a unprepared question based on it.

In the same sort of way we can interview the biblical text. We can question the text to discover the sort of things we want to know. Like any interviewer we need some questions prepared, but also need to feel free to take a new line of enquiry as the process unfolds.

So we might come with questions about the context of that passage of scripture, such as

> ☛ Who wrote this?
> ☛ Why was it written?
> ☛ Why was it written in this style?
> ☛ Who was the intended audience?
> ☛ What did the author wish to achieve?
> ☛ What might have been the result?

When Laurie Green was in a Birmingham parish he took an old method of asking questions of the text and improved it. What became know as the 'Spaghetti Junction Method' was used by both individuals and groups.

Why don't you try the Spaghetti Junction Method for the next few days in your own personal devotions? You will find it outlined in the margin.

SPAGHETTI JUNCTION CHECKLIST

LIGHT – What things in the passage illuminate or inspire you?

QUESTION – What things don't you understand?

SURPRISE – What things in the passage surprise you?

APPROVAL – What things do you agree with, and approve of?

REJECT – What are you turned off by, reject or question?

PARALLEL – Can you name something like it from elsewhere in the bible?

INPUT – Can you name something like it from you own life and experience?

ACTION – What are you prompted to do as a result of this passage?

Restricted by knowledge

I remember once being interviewed about the church of which I was minister. A regional newspaper had picked up that we had seen considerable growth. They wanted a story, and I thought it should be easy enough to provide them with some information.

The best way of telling the story might have been to include some stories of the people whose lives had been changed, but the reporter was too busy to talk to them. The interviewer also didn't know enough about church life to ask even the most simple questions that made sense. In the end all that resulted was a story about how we had been forced into putting extra chairs into the church to accommodate people on Sundays.

We need to know something about the bible to be able to interview the text intelligently. We have to study the background and the context of the biblical text in order to guard against asking the wrong kinds of questions. So alongside our devotional reading and our reflection on the text, we need to be increasing our knowledge of the bible as a whole. Like good TV and newspaper interviewers, we need to do our homework.

Restricted by culture

Another disadvantage is that the sort of questions we ask are conditioned by our culture and not that of the text. Like the interviewer, the questions we are really interested in may be very different from those behind that part of scripture. This is a perilous exercise because, unless done well, we may find ourselves claiming scriptural authority for things that scripture did not intend to say.

But we can ask questions that help us take off our cultural spectacles, such as

> ☛ How is this passage understood in our culture?
> ☛ How might it have been understood differently in the culture in which it was written?
> ☛ How might it be understood differently in another culture today?

From the LUMKO institute in South Africa comes this group study material. You will note that the material is designed not for addressing individual issues but community ones. It is a good example of group theological reflection starting from scripture.

You may have come across other ways of addressing the text better. Describe them in your journal and write down how they have helped you.

MORE...

Further questions of the text might include
☛ At thetime of writing what situation might have caused the writer to think that this particular bit was too important to be left out?

For an epistle
☛ Where does this fit in the argument?
☛ What arguments would have been used by those who disagreed?

For prophecy
☛ Who would have cheered hearing this?
☛ Who would have booed?

LUMKO

Today we follow a Bible-method called 'Group Response'. We shall *not share with each other how the Word of God has touched us personally. Today we think of our community, the problems we have together in our parish, village, town or country. After we have read the text of the Bible we shall ask the question: 'Which problem in our community is mentioned in the text? What is God's will for us in a group?'*

1. We read the text
☛ We read the text twice.
☛ We pick out words or phrases – read them aloud and keep silence in between these phrases.

2. Which problems of our community are mentioned in the text?
☛ Let us now discuss in little groups. Each one should talk to his immediate neighbour. We discuss the following question: 'Which problems of our parish, village, town or country are similar to the problems mentioned in the text?' The same question in other words: 'The text reminds us of which problems in our own community?'
☛ We discuss this question for five minutes.
☛ After five minutes each group reports back.
☛ Let us choose one problem which we are going to discuss further.

3. What does God tell us about our problem?
☛ We keep silence for about three minutes. During this time of silence we ask ourselves: 'What did God tell us in our text? What does he tell us about our problem?'
☛ After three minutes: We tell each other what we think God is advising us about our problem.

4. What does God want us to do?
WHO will do WHAT and WHEN?

The same question can be asked by an individual studying the bible. 'Which problems of my parish, village, town or country are similar to the problems mentioned in the text?'

A HISTORY OF EMERGING TRUTH

In the last few pages we have looked at Christian reflection when the starting point is the bible. Now we investigate the use of other starting points from faith. The church has much to draw on: years of doctrinal formulation, martyrs for the faith and their history, day by day worship over three millennia, ignominious failure and amazing glory.

All this wealth is part of our inheritance. We can use this wealth as a resource for theological reflection. In doing so we look for patterns in the material, insights from the experience, recurring detail, and developing understanding. Some of these perceptions from Christian history will have biblical parallels and some will not.

You may have questions about using this kind of material. Most of us, as children of the Reformation, hold tenaciously that scripture is paramount and that the church's tradition is not to be put on a par with the bible. So we have to be careful that what we learn does not contradict the truths we find in the bible. However we are all the losers if we then ignore what has been learnt over the last two thousand years. We can take seriously Jesus' words that the Spirit will lead Christian people into all truth, and therefore expect that the church's story will show signs of that emerging truth.

Here are three examples of that emerging truth and which can offer parallels to be used in our Christian thinking.

A lesson from history

John Newton (1725 -1807) may be most famous for his hymn *Amazing Grace*. He spent ten years of his life in the slave trade, shipping slaves from Africa to the Americas. He was converted during a shipwreck off Newfoundland. He continued in the trade for some years, eventually giving it up for a shore job at Liverpool. He was later ordained and became an opponent of the slave trade. In his opposition of the trade he influenced William Wilberforce who spearheaded the fight in parliament that eventually outlawed it.

John Newton's life shows a significant pattern to us. It consists of the person who
♦   is thoroughly involved in something wrong
♦   is converted
♦   grasps a new understanding (which may come very slowly)
♦   can speak with utter conviction of the evils involved
♦   is a vital awareness raiser for the church
♦   enables the evil to be diminished

Like me, you may have heard fearsome tales of people who have come out of awful situations. Some, like Newton, have been expected to take part in morally wrong acts in the work place. If their testimony can be used to inform public opinion and change the law, then their experience may not be wasted.

One could also cite Augustine on the misuse of sexuality and Francis of Assisi on the misuse of riches.

A lesson from theology

A recurring theme in theology is our 'creatureliness' or 'earthiness'. One example is the Eastern Orthodox church's deliberations about the use of icons. Over the first few centuries of the church there was heated discussion.

♦ On one side were those who prohibited any representation of Christ, concerned that veneration soon turns to worship. They also believed that in a painting none of his divinity could be captured. Any pictures of Him would therefore deny his divinity.

♦ On the other side were those who believed that icons were a positive affirmation of the incarnation. They spoke of the intention of God that matter be sanctified. They agreed that you do have to be careful not to worship the picture, but you can use it as a window into heaven.

Eventually the latter view won the day and the decision was formalised at the second council of Nicaea in 787 AD.

The recurring theme is the temptation to spiritualise the gospel to the point where it loses touch with human creatureliness. In this temptation humanity, matter and creation are to be denied. This is an aberration of purity – being aloof from the world. At its best the church affirms the world as belonging to God (though not underestimating its sinfulness) and seeks its redemption.

This temptation has a most serious ethical side as shown in this Snoopy cartoon from *The Gospel according to Peanuts*.

Copyright©
United Features
Syndicate, Inc.
Reproduced by
permission.

A lesson from worship

Those who have written forms of worship are aware of the value of the patterns becoming instilled into people. For instance, the forms of Morning Prayer from the Book of Common Prayer, the Alternative Service Book or Celebrating Common Prayer have similar patterns. They move from confession to hearing the word of God. Then follows response and lastly intercession.

This is an invaluable pattern for a life of prayer, discovered through many generations. It is also like the process of our salvation.

This pattern of daily prayer can help us discern the appropriate response to situations where something has gone wrong. We confess it, hear the new way following God's law, we respond in faith and pray for strength to sustain the new way.

TOO PURE?

Similar issues might be seen in:
☛ the Gnostics in the second century
☛ the dismissal of music from puritan churches
☛ the medieval espousal of celibacy as a 'higher' form of life.

One comes across it constantly in the church:
☛ 'We cannot work with *them* because we might get contaminated.'
☛ 'We cannot have dance in church; someone may get aroused.'
☛ 'He's no church leader, I saw him crying.'

PATTERNS

Can you think of other examples of prevalent patterns in church history, theology or worship? Note them down. It is important to have a large enough store of patterns for when we have to choose parallels to our experience.

To get you started what about:

☛ People whom 'the authorities' said were wrong and were persecuted, but who proved in the fullness of time to be right. E.g. Joan of Arc.

☛ There is a 'now and not yet' quality about the Christian life. We are 'saved' now and yet wait for it in its fullness in heaven. (When thinking about this note what happens when the paradox is avoided and a person or church totally concentrates on one or the other.)

YOUR OWN CONNECTIONS

We now come to the point where it will again be useful for you to write down some thoughts and insights which are significant to you, this time starting from the perspective of the Faith.

Connections from the Bible

There will have been times when the biblical text has given you new insight on your experience. It may not have come in a structured way as you sat praying one day, it may have been more a flash of inspiration as you sat on the bus.

♦ Perhaps a parable suddenly seemed to have a parallel in your present experience.

♦ It might have been a new connection between different passages of scripture, so that they brought light on each other *and* on the present day.

♦ A character may suddenly have seemed to resemble you, or someone else.

♦ It might be that you saw Jesus deal with a person in a way that you had not previously noticed.

So try to write about a particular biblical text which helped you in this way, quoting the passage and what in particular came home to you about it. In about 300 words note down:

☞ what was significant
☞ what the new insight was
☞ how the insight came (through feelings, though what someone said, from 'thin air')
☞ what was the value to you of the new ideas
☞ how it connected with your own life

It may also be important to note:

☞ what sort of *occasion* it was (personal devotions, bible study in a group, sermon, tape)
☞ what *method* of study was used on this occasion (might the method used have made a difference to the way you understood the text?)

We will leave the 'how it made a difference' until later in the workbook. Then you may discover more ways in which that passage could connect with your own life.

Connections from the Christian tradition

I now want you to do a second exercise, this time remembering an occasion when something from Christian tradition *other than the bible* was the source of a new Christian insight.

The insight may have come as you
♦ read a book
♦ sat looking at a stained glass window
♦ heard a piece of sacred music

If you cannot think of anything, you can use the material on pages 54-55:
♦ Is there anyone you know who has gone through a similar process to John Newton?
♦ Can you think of situations where you are tempted to deny your humanity?
♦ When did you last use the pattern of confession through to intercession on something major in your life?

Write about the experience in about 300 words, noting in particular what it was that suddenly made connections for you:
☛ what the experience was
☛ what struck you as significant
☛ what the new connection was
☛ how the connection came (through an idea, though what you heard, from the Spirit)
☛ what the value to you was of the new ideas
☛ where it connected with your own life

Again we leave the issues of what *difference* it made to you until later in the workbook. Likewise it may be important to note under what *circumstance* the new ideas came. Was the situation significant in the discovery?

Evaluating the process

When you have done this writing it will be important for you to start making some judgement on the process for you.

♦ What helps and what hinders?
♦ What sorts of connection are easy and what ones are hard?
♦ Are there any you feel proud of making?
♦ Any of which you are ashamed?

We all make connections that later we consider not very appropriate. Maybe we get greater insight as the years go by. Sometimes have to revise our views quite radically as new information becomes available.

> **Making mistakes is all part of our journey in life. They are to be noted, and repentance made. But we must not start avoiding situations in which mistakes might be made.**

For example we may hear **John** making a sharp criticism of someone to Pat and later read that we 'will be judged with the judgement we make'. So we decide that John may have been a little off track. But we may hear later that in doing what he did John enabled Pat to avoid following a wrong example, and sense that we made a mistake in our perception of John.

USING ART

Religious art is a valuable resource. I remember being shown a little known Rembrant drawing of the head of Jesus which touched me deeply as it resonated in me His humanity, especially His strength in vulnerability.

What art touches you? What religious art do you like? Does remembering what you appreciate tell you anything about what is important for you in the Christian faith?

THE LATIN LINK

Theology is a task for the church world-wide, and for every denomination. Many insights to help us think in new ways as Christians, come from Latin America. Liberation Theology was born there and this kind of Christian reflection has given us useful patterns – and enabled us to note some dangers.

The background

In the early 19th century many of the countries of South America gained their independence from European colonial powers. Mostly their official religious affiliation was, and still is, to the Roman Catholic church, which had come in the wake of the conquest by Spain and Portugal. (In this there are many parallels with Britain, sub-Saharan Africa and the missionary movement to it.) Although politically independent they have continued to be under economic domination, first by Europe and more latterly by North America.

They display the poverty of many two-third's world countries. Though initially subsistence rural economies these nations now host huge shanty towns round enormous cities. It is typical for the wealth to be owned by a small elite who control the political and judicial life of these countries.

In the 1960s some priests in Latin America began to question the church's role in shoring up the existing state of political and economic affairs. Vatican Two opened up new possibilities. In the countries themselves economists were recognising that the theories by which development leads to economic advancement were highly questionable. A new sense of identity was being formed also in cultural affairs. Liberation was the buzz word.

The programme

Some priests and educationalists recognised that if there were to be true 'liberation' for people it could not come by revolution. In their view revolution exchanged the names of the rulers and political prisoners but did precious little for the ordinary person. **A true liberation could only come as the people at the bottom of the pile were able to value themselves and their contribution to society.** Only then could they insist on the changes that would bring a better life.

This programme did not find universal appeal. It had the strongest opponents in those who might lose their influence or wealth. The Roman Catholic bishops felt they could only give lukewarm assent, especially given the Vatican's wariness. The programme used some of the tools of Marxist analysis and so it was easy to label the whole enterprise 'Marxist' and discredit it.

A COKE SCANDAL

In the main street of one capital city in South America in spring 1989 I sat down at a smart cafe table and ordered a Coke. Such was the consequences of the debt crisis and the exchange rate situation that the cost to me was one-twentieth of what it would have been in England. At the side of the table was a legless beggar collecting on his patch.

The method

The key tool in this work was the use of small groups. In an oppressive regime individuals on their own are too vulnerable. These groups, formed in parishes and neighbourhoods, were enabled by priests or nuns. These helpers were convinced of the need, under God, for people to find salvation not just in the next life but in this. These groups became known as 'base communities'.

These communities consistently use one form of theological reflection. The theologians who have written about them insist that reflection without action is an unhelpful luxury, and action without reflection is defective. They urge that reflection and action in concert is needed. They give this the title *praxis*.

> **'Many theologians insist that ortho-praxis (right acting) is ultimately more important than ortho-doxy (right doctrine).'**
> Philip Berryman in *Liberation Theology*

Within the base communities the bible is used as an aid to discovering appropriate behaviour in the light of the realities of experience. The group spends much time talking through the experience of life, analysing it and identifying issues. The Bible is used to illuminate the experience, reflect on it and discover God's perspective on it.

Use of the Bible

Some biblical passages and motifs have been used much:
- the liberation of the Exodus
- the death and resurrection of Jesus
- the theme of creation with its concerns over the dignity of humanity, the value of work, the 'ownership' of land, and the relationships of men and women
- passages which point towards what later became known as 'God's preferential option for the poor'
- Jesus's challenge to love one's enemies.

However the results of this group reflection are not complete in themselves. Action is necessary. Holding together their experience and the scriptures, they then move on to a discussion on what is to be *done*. In the light of God seeking the liberation of the poor, what action is appropriate? Practical proposals are made. At the least this will be support for the individuals on the forefront of the issues. At the other extreme it may be collective action to confront injustice, form an economic co-operative, or demand health care.

Such action has brought much liberation. There has often been a sense of God acting with and for the base community in its battles for right. Like any authentic action of the church there have been many martyrs.

Liberation Theology has taught the world-wide church much about reading the scriptures through the eyes of the poor. It has caused many to re-evaluate which themes are important in the scriptures. It has also challenged the Church about models for Christian action which start 'from the bottom up'. In our quest for good theological reflection it provides a well-tested model for a group which wants to think (and act) in more thoroughly Christian ways.

KEY TEXT

A key text might be the quotation from Isaiah 61, used by Jesus in his sermon in Nazareth (Luke 4:18f):
The Spirit of the Lord is upon me because he has anointed me; he has sent me to announce good news to the poor, to proclaim release for the prisoners and recovery of sight for the blind; to let the broken victims go free; to proclaim the year of the Lord's favour.

GROUP THEOLOGY
– AND ACTION

Latin America is not the only setting in which groups have 'done theology'. Over the last few decades there have been constant attempts to encourage it in the industrialised countries of Europe and North America. The creation of meaningful groups within the mainstream churches has often been a by-product of dividing a large congregation into smaller units. These groups, whether primarily for fellowship, learning or prayer, have sometimes also engaged in serious theological reflection.

Certain attitudes are required for groups to engage in theological reflection.

♦ They have to value real human experience whether it seems to fit theological categories or not.
♦ They have to be open to the treasures of the faith speaking to corporate situations as well as to personal ones.

For more information about the value of Latin American style base communities in Europe and North America, see Margaret Hebblethwaite's book *Basic is Beautiful* (Fount, 1993).

YOUR GROUP?

Think about some of the Christian groups to which you belong or have belonged.
☛ What happened when someone was joyful or expressed a need?
☛ Was there any particular person in the group who gave permission for a celebration to take place or for uncomfortable things to be talked over?
☛ Was anyone a censor preventing the group expressing itself?

AN EXAMPLE FROM AFFLUENT ENGLAND

I was once part of a housegroup in a church in an affluent area of England. We were nearing the time for the Annual General Meeting and the previous year's accounts had been published. Some members of the group were very concerned about what they showed. We took time to hear what the real issue was. Eventually we recognised that the problem for these members was that the church seemed so mean. The accounts of the Church Council showed that very little money had been given away, and that somehow all its money was used for its own (good) purposes: the minister's salary, the church building, the organ and choir, the church hall.

The group turned to the scriptures. There seemed to be much in the Acts about great generosity from poor churches to poorer ones. There were allusions in the Old Testament law about leaving the gleanings in the field, which encouraged an attitude of not using all one's resources for oneself. There seemed to be a challenge to the church to use only part of our resources on ourselves and give some to other causes. The group decided that it could not leave the issue there. It had to take it to the Church Council.

The debate was polite Christian trench warfare. It was recognised by all that individuals from the church gave away large sums of money. The Council's view was that it needed more rather than less. The housegroup's view was that it would never get any more while it was perceived to be so tight-fisted.

Eventually some way forward was found. It was agreed that the Council would give away a goodly proportion of its income whilst safeguarding its statutory obligations. It was also agreed to sponsor a particular and significant piece of charitable work with which the church already had links. Surprisingly (to the Council's members, but not to the housegroup's) enough money flowed into the Council's coffers which more than offset what it had agreed to give away.

KEYS
TO GOOD
REFLECTION

CONTENTS

PURPOSE

The purpose of this Unit is to begin the process of interpreting our experience and our initial reflections on it.

THE WOOD FOR THE TREES

REVIEW

In the previous Unit we began to write about situations as we saw them, carefully noting the feelings, facts and attitudes involved (see pages 40-41, 46). We noted too that it is important to write it down before going on to interpret what we experience.

Can you remember the reasons why writing is important? For the answers see page 37.

So far we have tried to interpret our experience as little as possible. That is not wholly possible because in selecting the material to write we have begun an interpretation. The fact that some material did not get in means we decided that those facts and feelings were not important enough.

There is no such thing as 'facts, all the facts and nothing but the facts'! The selection of information about facts, feelings and attitudes was itself a start on the road to interpretation. The identification of what is significant is the next step.

In this Unit I will introduce you to some of the ways in which you can help yourself to
◆ check you have *sufficient* information
◆ make the distinction between information and *significant* information

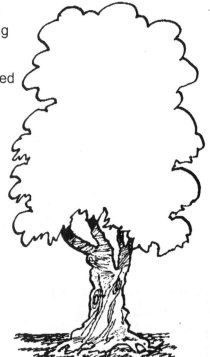

Sufficient

First you need to check you have written down all the information you need. Are there gaps that need to be filled if you are to have a full picture? In your selection you are being interpretative. But equally you cannot spend too long gathering, for even if you had all the time in the world you would never have all the information.

Here is a checklist that might help.

Who? Is there a social dimension that needs to be understood? Have I noted all those involved and their inter-relationships?

Where? Have I got the geography clear? What are the connections between where things took place?

When? Have I got the history of this sorted out in my mind? Are there patterns that I should note?

What? Have I got a grasp of the analysis and connections of material things – money, power, politics?

Which? Are there different sides to which the various people are committed?

Why? Are there deeper 'spiritual' issues in all this? Is there another level of 'why?' which I am not seeing?

How? How does this material inter-relate – the people, the history, the spiritual?

Significant

Now you have a sufficient body of information the question comes, 'What are the really significant things here?' There is no simple answer. There is no guaranteed way of discerning the significant. If there were, then many more people would use it and have far greater wisdom. The world is full of people offering fragments of the truth without offering the clues to assessing the value of it.

I offer you four avenues that may help this assessment.

If you place on paper your feelings as well as the facts, you will have a better discernment about the whole. The inconsistencies in the facts will show up. You will be able to make a better judgement on the appropriateness of your feelings. You will be better able to attend to the effect of your attitudes on what we experienced. Just having it down on paper will increase your objectivity and therefore the value of any assessment you make of your experience.

WHAT'S MISSING?

In some situations the 'significant information' may be what is *not* said. Reading testimonials or references for employment one has to carry a check list of topics that *should* be mentioned (e.g. timekeeping, health, attitudes to colleagues). If something is missing it can often mean the writer is actually conveying that this has been a problem – but is not prepared to write anything negative.

If you re-read your own writing occasionally, this will cause some evaluation to awaken in you. There will be feelings that emerge: surprise, fear, embarrassment. There will come a gradual awareness that some facts don't fit in easily and will have to be looked at more, others that fade into the background and others that gradually stand out. Each of these responses will also carry with it some evaluation.

If you talk over the issues with someone else, your own feelings will become more measured in the conversation. Since your views are down on paper you will be able to hear better what the other person says without the distraction of holding on to your own ideas. As the conversation proceeds you will come to a new evaluation of the information.

You can expect the Spirit to be active to help you discern, and you can pray for this. He can illuminate your mind so that the realities begin to emerge. Try to read the material conscious of the Spirit's presence, and note His response.

JUST HOW I SEE IT

Just as the choice of information reveals something of yourself, so the identification of what is significant reflects your personality. The knowledge of that predisposition and its effect will be also be helpful. Try to get to know what imbalances you will bring with you to any situation. To be honest before God about this means to value your own predisposition and at the same time look more closely for evidence that points elsewhere (especially if it directly contradicts your own starting point).

The opposite to your natural inclinations is often a very fruitful area in which to hunt for what is significant. The material is not familiar and it will be that much harder to make judgements about it, but it will add greatly to the balance of your understanding.

PREVIEW

To help identify key issues I have included in this Unit some tools. In the next pages you will read about
☛ art forms
☛ personality types
☛ connectedness
The use of each of these can assist the process of recognising the key issues.

APPRECIATING OUR WEAKNESSES

One of the stranger aspects of the spiritual life is that often God seems to use our weaknesses as the medium through which to speak to us. I suspect it is because we have dealt with life using our strengths, and this has left too much debris belonging to our pride and self-sufficiency. We automatically use our strong points. If our usual mode of having 'God thoughts' does not yield much insight, then it may be that we have to find a way forward that uses our weaker attributes.

When doing something new we tend to concentrate on our favoured ways of thinking. If we think logically we tend to try to think even more logically than usual. If we think laterally we look for even more bizarre connections.

I recently moved house and needed to plan the garden. My natural inclination was to reach for paper and pencil and ask myself what I will use the garden *for*, before drawing it out as a plan. That may give perfectly good results. But if I become stuck it might be better if I start all over again, this time imagining some of my favourite flowers and where I might like them.

The tools and techniques on these pages are to help you identify more readily the significant issues of an experience you have written up. They are examples of what can be helpful; you might have others to add.

IMAGINATION

On these pages we have suggested some ideas that use our creativity. This can be disconcerting to those of us who are children of the Reformation, because we like to hold onto revealed truth and tend to treat other facets of the truth as suspect. This can lead us to miss methods that are of great value – simply because they use the imagination.

If you are familiar with the spiritual exercises of St Ignatius, you will know that they use the connections between the imagination and the spiritual to help one into a story. In the practice of meditation much use is made of imagining every detail of the biblical account. Both the perspective taken and the unfolding action are significant for understanding yourself and what God wishes to say to you. In the same way your imagination can be unlocked to help you in trying to identify the significant facts of a situation.

If you take time to imagine what it looks like from someone else's point of view, you may perceive it differently. Try imagining Jesus walking into the scene. Let your imagination run on to discover what he might do or say.

The results can be keys in understanding what seems significant to you.

Drawing

I had the distinction at school of always being at the bottom of the class for art. Whatever else might happen in the report from school that bit was certain. But that does not mean that art is useless to me. Sometimes it is easier for me to draw a diagram or paint a picture of something, even if it is stick men and cotton wool sheep. The resulting art may be so embarrassing that I will let no-one see it, but it might illuminate the situation I am thinking about with great clarity.

Through drawing we can identify keys to understanding in a way that ten thousand words can never do.

Story

It can be liberating for our interpretation of our experience if it is turned into story. Story form liberates us from having to ensure reality at all times. Of especial value is something on the lines of a children's nursery story ('Once upon a time…'), or in the style of science fiction where time and distance can be reversed.

Translation into story is especially helpful because it often yields a literary link with a biblical narrative.

Engineering

All branches of human endeavour can give us ways into seeing things afresh or discovering what is significant. It may be that the situation seems to resemble one of those fantasy clocks in which at the hour all sorts of funny things happen. A wooden person pops out here, a whistle goes off there, doors open to reveal their secrets, yet all of the actions seem totally unrelated. Only the timing gives the clue. A look behind the scenes will reveal that it is the same clockwork mechanism that caused them all to happen at once. If many things seem to happen coincidentally like the clock, it might be worth a careful study to discover if there were connections behind the scenes. Alternatively, you might make a few guesses about the connection and go looking for evidence.

If the arts are your natural arena, perhaps you could look for clues by noting similarities in the technological field.

Politics

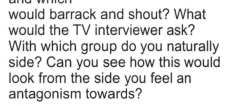

National and international politics can help you discover the significant. How would this issue look if dressed up in national politics? Which party would applaud from the benches, and which would barrack and shout? What would the TV interviewer ask? With which group do you naturally side? Can you see how this would look from the side you feel an antagonism towards?

When the issues are written up on the large canvas we sometimes see significances that are otherwise hidden from us.

LEFT/RIGHT

It is not only in spiritual things that we might address our weaknesses. I am naturally right handed and from very early was able to catch a ball in that hand easily. The coach to the cricket team used to remind us that we needed to catch the ball with either hand. He said it was more important for me to learn to catch it with my left hand than to catch it better with my right.

What are your strengths? What are your weaknesses? What techniques would accord with your weaknesses?

PERSONAL STORIES: 2

This Unit is about finding the key issues. To illustrate this we continue our stories from pages 38-39. You may need to refresh your memory of them before you read further.

In these stories there are some very difficult moral dilemmas. The resolutions have come after much spiritual agonising, sometimes over many years. You may have faced dilemmas equally problematic. You may not. Even if you do not share their views you can learn much from these people about their method of working.

What are your reactions to the second episode of these stories? Try writing it down in your journal.

Alison

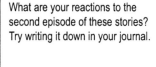

The issue of power was important to me, albeit I did not realise why for a long time. I used my position of power in order to have some sense of security. I was less likely to be challenged if I was obviously in control, and it also gave me a sense of self-worth. I was brought up in a strict Puritanical home where I never seemed to be able to quite reach the expected 'mark' of either my parents or the church, in which I constantly felt guilty at not being 'good enough'.

I left the church in my early 20s and remained out of the church for many many years. During this period, I developed the sense of having to be in control of my own life. So gradually I built up the use of power which became part of me. It enabled me to retain the wall I had built around myself, and to continue to be in control of my feelings. It enabled me to stop listening to my conscience, and to do what I wanted to do, without regard for the hurt this may have caused others. It let me stop thinking about my past and attempt to forget the past. I sought and gained promotion, wanting to climb to 'the top of the tree' in my profession. I disliked losing at anything! No wonder God wanted to take this part of my life! As I slowly returned to His care, then He showed me more and more of the need to change.

I COULDN'T POSSIBLY!

One of the first reactions we often have to the prompts of heaven is, 'I couldn't possibly! Many of the most significant stories of Christian living or mission have at their heart the moment when the monolithic wall 'I couldn't possibly' is seen to have a tiny breach in it. Someone begins to ask whether God might be asking them to…

The problem as we see it could be resources or circumstances. Our difficulties become even worse when our reaction emanates from our ethical views. We then have every possible argument on our side for *inaction*. However, we have to remember that God sometimes takes us outside what we previously considered 'correct'.

There are plenty of examples in the scriptures. Remember that Jesus, when challenged about his behaviour, quoted the story of David and the Holy Bread (Matthew 12:3, 1 Samuel 21:6). God's view of his specific commandments seems similar to his view of his laws in nature. We call it a miracle when He adapts the laws of nature on individual occasions. There seem to be occasions when he does the same with specific ethical demands when this is necessary to bring about His wider purposes! What long-running argument in the gospels is about this?

Tony and Jayne

I wrestled deeply with the issues which life was presenting. I felt frustrated that I did not know what to do. I continually prayed but never had the 'writing on the wall' that would make it abundantly clear what we should do. It seemed to me that much of our life was not quite right, but nothing seemed really wrong enough to need to change it drastically. I took my cue from the American saying, 'If it ain't broke, don't fix it.'

I was also aware, though somewhat dimly, that my background had left me with a need to get everything right. As a child I had learnt to be a 'good boy'. I knew God always left room for faith, so it was unlikely that we would receive guidance clear enough to avoid doubt. There seemed to be enough direction from God but it felt awfully scary to think of making changes as a result.

I wondered about ordination. I had thought of it many years ago and made enquiries, but by now I knew (quite a relief) that I was too old to give up work and study towards full time church employment. Being out of sympathy with the local church did not help this because we all knew I could not tolerate the idea of working more closely with them.

I had noted that one of the key issues for Jayne was our elder son's intuitive sense that whenever life went wrong he would be bailed out or come 'home'. He was very uncomfortable with the style of life we led and the capitalist system it embodied, but whenever life became too tough he was there making demands and taking help. The whole environment was soaked with memories. Jayne often felt that somewhere she had made a big mistake in bringing him up.

Key: Guidance always leaves room for doubt and faith.

Key: More church work is impossible.

Key: A dependant son of thirty needs to be 'independent' --whatever the consequences

Sarah

I had prayed and agonised over a long period, not knowing what the honourable Christian response should be, and was very frightened to face the consequences of any decisions. I knew that God hates divorce, and it is not his will for us, but in his mercy he does allow it.

One key issue was about truth, both inwardly and outwardly.

Fact 1. I needed to face the truth that our marriage really had broken down beyond all restoration, and that I had failed again - we had both failed. Failure of a second marriage, blessed by the church, seemed an enormously difficult fact for me to accept.

Fact 2. My health was suffering under the continual stress.

Fact 3. The public nature of Jeremy's amorous activities was causing acute embarrassment. There was growing awareness of this by others who were very concerned, as was our family.

Fact 4. I was by no means certain that I could cope with life on my own after relinquishing all financial claims on my husband, including future pension rights.

A second key issue was about decision making. Any decision had to be totally on my own. I could not put any weight of responsibility on anyone else, particularly the children. It would be unfair even to discuss it with them at any length. I felt very isolated, and deliberately stood back a little from friends and family during this time.

A third key issue was one of trust. I desperately wanted to do the honourable thing, to be able to stand with Christian dignity through any amount of trouble. I needed to rely on the integrity of my faith, to trust that God would not turn away from me. This was new territory and I felt very vulnerable. Would the rope hold?

On pages 40-41 I asked you to write the first stage of three reflections. Now you should write the second stage of each of them trying to formulate what is the significant information and which are the key issues. You should aim for 300 to 500 words for each of the three. This will take you some time and you should not go on with the workbook until you have completed it.

USING YOUR DARKER SIDE

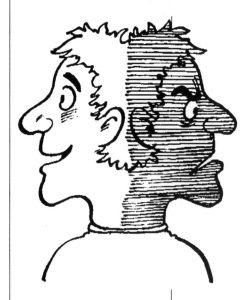

Another way to look afresh at a situation is to choose to view it through a different facet of our personality.

There are many ways of categorising human personality. Ones in common use in the church are Myers-Briggs and the Ennegram. The many tests presently used in the workplace testify to their perceived value. (We have also to beware of the limitations of these tests; they are no panacea for all our ills!)

If you have taken one of these tests and know the result you might remember which category you fitted into. You might also recall the other categories to which you did not belong. The technique I am suggesting here is to look at the data through the lens of one of the other categories. The difference of perspective can give a whole new understanding.

In the following examples I am drawing on the personality test that I know best, Myers-Briggs. I will also start from the biblical story. The method holds good for the other categorisations of human personality.

Detail instead of patterns

You might be a person who tends most of all to notice the patterns in things. Reading the scriptures you are gripped by the overall themes. You trace the hand of God in the patterns of experience of Israel or in the gospels. It might be easy for you to relate to the big themes written

up on page 49. You don't take too much notice of the detail.

If this describes you then you might like to make a change for a while and look much more closely at the text. You might become much more deliberate in noticing the detail, addressing it and seeking to learn from it. This can give quite a new perspective. Words, phrases, descriptions can spring out and captivate us. When we concentrate on these we might get a very different view of what is going on in the text. It may then have the possibility of connecting with the detail of everyday reality.

Detailing the Transfiguration

Imagine you are reflecting on the Transfiguration (Mark 9:2-8). If you were looking at the patterns you might note the need for Jesus to be strengthened before his walk to Jerusalem, and the significance of it being Moses and Elijah rather than Abraham and Isaiah. You might also note the foolishness of Peter who, as often in the gospels, spoke before thinking and wanted to cling tenaciously to the good experiences.

In your reflection you might note a situation you face that is very uncomfortable, and your need to be strengthened before meeting it. You might then decide that you need to spend some time alone with God beforehand so that you can be encouraged. You might note that like Peter you tend to cling to the good experiences for fear that once gone they will never be repeated. You might recognise that your local church is like this, living with past glories and unable to face today's challenges to move on.

However if you begin to look at the detail you might note the voice from the cloud saying, 'This is my Son, my beloved; listen to him.' *Listen to Him.* Listen to him even more than to the great law-giver or the foremost prophet. You might reflect that in that uncomfortable situation you face you need to listen to Him rather than all the other words that are spilled out. You have to have your attention on Him. Thus it might enable you to feel closer to Him. It might be that you can listen to his sayings about meekness and poverty of spirit. That may transform your approach.

You might note that Peter, in particular, needed to hear those words about listening to Jesus. Only recently at Caesarea Philippi he had chosen not to hear about the suffering to come and indeed to rebuke Jesus for insisting on its necessity. He needed to avoid worldly wisdom and listen to Jesus. In reflecting on this and on your church you might note the many situations when the church listens to worldly wisdom rather than God. It might be that, like Peter, it is being so insistent on continuing its ministry and proclaiming God's word that it cannot listen to Him who calls it to suffer, and perhaps, in some sense, to die.

Thinking or feeling

You might be a person who makes judgements on situations more by how you *feel* about them and your emotional reactions to them, rather than a cool hard thoughtful approach. In the biblical story you will have a sense of what the people felt and what made them react as they did. It might be easy for you to appreciate the agony of Gethsemane and the awesomeness of the Damascus Road, and not so easy for you to treasure the theological argument of Romans.

In the same way as I have shown above, you might like to begin to try deliberately to think as a Christian. Instead of noting what seems to come naturally about the feeling, how about trying to discover what was happening in *theological* terms in Gethsemane, or trying to appreciate the logic and approach

of that educated man who was transformed on the Damascus Road?

Thinking Gethsemane

Imagine you are reflecting on something that connects with Gethsemane. Your normal method might begin with an awareness of one of the feelings:
♦ impending doom
♦ betrayal
♦ fear of the future
♦ inadequate support from friends

If a reflection based directly on this awareness does not yield anything valuable, you might instead try a different approach. Still using the same connection, note if any of the theological issues around the Gethsemane experience are present. There are many but you might start with:
♦ the vulnerability of Jesus, showing His Father's vulnerability
♦ the resolution of the Son of God to go through pain if necessary
♦ the heavenly support when human agencies fail
Thinking about one of these might break the impasse.

TRY IT!

Try noting the feelings of the Damascus Road and then the theological issues surrounding it. If in a reflection you come across the same feelings, try using this technique of switching to the theological understanding.

Try a slightly different technique. Try to look at one of your favourite passages in the bible through the mind and heart of someone with a very different personality from yours.

OVERVIEWS AND DETAIL

Overviews and detail are both necessary.

On the North Devon coast path near Lynton there is a signpost. For each of the three directions the arms point the word written is 'Lynton'. Each qualifies the destination merely by a different route (e.g. 'by the coast path'). The signpost tells the truth – all paths lead to Lynton. Imagine yourself by that signpost wanting to go, not to Lynton, but to the next inlet, Lee Bay. Though it is not mentioned, one path leads there. To choose the right path you will need to have local knowledge or a map which gives an overview of the coast. Sometimes the detail, though true, conceals the wider picture.

On the other hand the overview on its own can sometimes be inadequate. On a walking holiday many years ago we were caught suddenly in mist on the top of one of the Lake District mountains. That day we had navigated using the relative positions of the other mountains. When the mist came down we were unable to see the other hills and so we were unable to verify our position. The visibility was about 100 yards and we could see the detail of the hill we were on. But, navigating by the other hills, we had not taken sufficient notice of the hill we were on and could recognise nothing that connected with the map. In effect we were lost. For safety's sake we ought to have been noticing more about the detail of our immediate position.

THE INTER-PERSPECTIVE

In this age of technology we are taught from school onwards that when we think about anything the way to begin is to analyse it. We break it down into small discrete pieces that are manageable. This workbook follows that principle. We have analysed what you need to know, broken it down into its component parts, thought about each one, written a little on each, and put it all together in a carefully ordered way.

This analytic method underpins most of the way that the Western world has developed over the last 300 years. By now most of us brought up in it assume it is not only right but the only way to proceed. However a moment to stop and think will remind us that, although this analytical method has brought us great gains, it has also brought the world to the brink of self-annihilation.

There are other ways of addressing the world. Several years ago I had the privilege of spending some time amongst the Cree Indians in Canada. When talking with them about their society I was told that it was built on 'respect' – respect for the natural world, respect for other human beings, respect for God. They may have been subjugated by the white man, but if he will ever listen they can teach him a realistic approach to ecology, as part of God's world, that may yet save humanity.

If, instead of analytical methods, we start looking for connections in our world the results may seem strange. For some theological reflection, this perspective is utterly vital. God has designed a created order in which 'all things are held together in Christ' (Colossians 1:17). It is best described in a fascinating piece by George Bebawi entitled Interbeing, on page 71.

When we take this standpoint and look for the connections between things we have not only a new perspective but a window into another world. You can make connections from your theological reflection into your spiritual growth. You can connect it, as I have in this workbook, with the insights of counselling. You can note similarities with the whole created order.

To trace one happening as connected with a second and the second with a third, though none is causative or dependent, may give very real clues to the realities behind what we see.

NO LINKS HERE!

A church was undergoing real trouble. The Vicar was described as being very authoritarian. Eventually a number of leaders left. Nearly half the Church Council and a quarter of the church members wanted the vicar to resign. In attempting some mediation I reminded Council members that the previous four vicars had all come and gone quickly, in as little as two years in one case, describing the parish as asking for stronger leadership. I put it to them that they now had what they had requested. Since they could not recognise a link between the past and the present, my words fell on deaf ears!

Look again at one of your reflections and re-work it with an accent on the connections, while avoiding analysis of the situation as much as you can. Remember that the connections may not only be in the experience side of it but also in the faith side of it.

INTERBEING

If you are a poet, you will see clearly that there is a cloud floating in this sheet of paper. Without a cloud, there will be no rain; without rain, the trees cannot grow; and without trees, we cannot make paper. The cloud is essential for the paper to exist. If the cloud is not here, the sheet of paper cannot be here either. So we can say that the cloud and the paper inter-are. 'Interbeing' is a word that is not in the dictionary yet, but if we combine the prefix 'inter-' with the verb 'to be', we have a new verb, inter-be. Without a cloud, we cannot have paper, so we can say that the cloud and the sheet of paper inter-are.

If we look into this sheet of paper even more deeply we can see the sunshine in it. If the sunshine is not there, the forest cannot grow. In fact, nothing can grow. Even we cannot grow without sunshine. And so, we know that the sunshine is also in this sheet of paper. The paper and the sunshine inter-are. And if we continue to look, we can see the logger who cut the tree and brought it to the mill to be transformed into paper. And we see the wheat. We know that the logger cannot exist without his daily bread, and therefore the wheat that became his bread is also in this sheet of paper. And the logger's father and mother are in it too. When we look in this way, we see that without all of these things, this sheet of paper cannot exist.

Looking even more deeply, we can see we are in it too. This is not difficult to see, because when we look at a sheet of paper, the sheet of paper is part of our perception. Your mind is in here and mine is also. So we can say that everything is in here with this sheet of paper. You cannot point out one thing that is not here - time, space, the earth, the rain, the minerals in the soil, the sunshine, the cloud, the river, the heat. Everything co-exists with this sheet of paper. That is why I think the word inter-be should be in the dictionary. 'To be' is to inter-be. You cannot just be by yourself alone. You have to inter-be with every other thing. This sheet of paper is, because everything else is.

Suppose we try to return one of the elements to its source. Suppose we return the sunshine to the sun. Do you think that this sheet of paper will be possible? No, without sunshine nothing can be. And if we return the logger to his mother, then we have no sheet of paper either. The fact is that this sheet of paper is made up only of 'non-paper elements'. And if we return these non-paper elements to their sources, then there can be no paper at all. Without 'non-paper elements', like mind, logger, sunshine and so on, there will be no paper. As thin as this sheet of paper is, it contains everything in the universe in it.

AN AFRICAN TALE

Finding the right key issues is crucial in theological reflection. The story and the quotations on these pages illustrate this dramatically.

Vincent J. Donovan was a missionary. As an American Roman Catholic priest he went to Tanzania in East Africa. He was attached to the Loliondo Mission in 1965. After a year of traditional missionary work to the Masai he asked if he could leave the mission-run hospital and schools. He believed that although the influence of the mission was great in material, educational and health terms, there was essentially no influence on the Masai's religious thinking. He did not know of any Masai adult who was Christian as a result of the mission's 20 year work.

He went to the Masai. He encouraged them to talk with him about their religious beliefs. He shared with them about his. He began to use their thought forms in speaking of his God. As he did so he became more aware of the cultural questions relating to religion. He noted how easily, in both Africa and the western world, people made God into their own tribal deity, a God who was always on their side in politics and conflict.

He became aware of the inherent conservatism of the Masai. Everything that needed to be known was handed down, accepted and learnt. This made the concept of new ideas a challenge and a threat. To think creatively about religion or human relationships was almost beyond their experience.

For many years he engaged in 'theological reflection'. As he listened he discovered parallels in their culture for Christian understandings of sin, forgiveness, sacraments, and new covenants. He found concepts in the Masai culture to express the notion of 'faith'. He noted the real questions they asked about life its meaning.

He discovered that, because of their culture, love for the people of the next village was a near impossibility. He had to ask himself whether it was possible for people in their culture to be evangelised individually or whether evangelism had to be to the Masai as a group. He questioned whether baptism was appropriate for individuals or whether it had to be the whole group – or none.

He wrote, 'Goodness and kindness and holiness and grace and divine presence and creating power and salvation were here before I got here. Even the fuller understanding of God's revelation to man, of the gospel, of the salvic act that had been accomplished once and for all for the human race was here before I got here.'

He discerned his task of evangelism by first discovering in their culture all the ideas and images that resonated with his understanding of Christianity. He reflected on them and noted where he would have to adapt the imagery to speak of his faith. He frequently found that he had to show that his God was different to the one they worshipped. He tried to find concepts and thought forms that would allow him to speak about Jesus and use the gospel stories.

His reflection was not only about the Masai. It caused him to think about the communities of faith from which he had come. He was concerned that the church preached about mission as being about Christ – and yet it seemed more interested in church membership.

The following quotations from his book show his reflection at its best.

On forgiveness

While I was going about the evangelising of these first villages, I noticed from time to time, a man on the outskirts of the different communities… He seemed poorer than the average Masai, and he did not seem to belong to any of the communities… afterward, I found out who he was. He was a man who had committed a great sin against the taboos of the Masai tribe. So he had become an outcast, belonging to no community. No community wanted him or was willing to have him live and work with them. A man with sin on his head would bring nothing but evil on any community with which he lived. The worst part of it was that the sin in question was unforgivable. There was no forgiveness possible from God or man… No wonder he asked me if I and my people could bring forgiveness… This man and his people knew all about sin. What they did not know was forgiveness of sin. They did not know that it was possible.

On faith

I was sitting talking with a Masai elder about the agony of belief and unbelief… He pointed out that the word… used to convey 'faith' was not a very satisfactory word in the language. It meant literally 'to agree to'. I myself knew the word had that shortcoming. He said 'to believe' like that was similar to a white hunter shooting an animal with his gun from a great distance. Only his eyes and his fingers took part in the act. We should find another word.

He said for a man really to believe is like a lion going after its prey. His nose and eyes and ears pick up the prey. His legs give him the speed to catch it. All the power of his body is involved in the terrible death leap and single blow to the neck with the front paw, the blow that actually kills. And as the animal goes down the lion envelopes it in his arms (Africans refer to the front legs of an animal as  its arms), pulls it to himself, and makes it part of himself. This is the way a lion kills. This is the way a man believes. This is what faith is.

IS UNITY GOOD NEWS?

European and American communities can be so individualistic as to make the notion of belonging to a group quite anathema to those who have grown up in them. We note the consumerism towards church life – 'I go to that one because it feels comfortable.' The biblical imagery of unity in which we have a common mind and all agree is beyond our wildest nightmares! Yet it is part of the gospel.

In what ways might this unity, which we instinctively feel chokes us, be good news?

On God

'We did not search you out, Padri,' he said to me. 'We did not even want you to come to us. You searched us out. You followed us away from your house into the bush, into the plains, into the steppes where our cattle are, into the hills where we take our cattle for water, into our villages, into our homes. You told us of the High God, how we must search for him, even leave our land and our people to find him. But we have not done this. We have not left our land. We have not searched for him. He has searched for us. He has searched us out and found us. All the time we think we are the lion. In the end, the lion is God.'

These quotations are from Vincent J. Donovan *Christianity Rediscovered, An Epistle from the Masai* (SCM Press, 1978). You might like to read the whole book.

AND YOU?

All communities have their own thought forms which can help or hinder the gospel being communicated. Thinking of another community you know, can you reflect what hinders the gospel being communicated in their thought forms? In this instance another community may be people from a different class or background.

WORLD STORIES: 2

We now have the second part of the stories of reflections that began on pages 44-45. Each of these concern issues than are wider than personal or family situations. At this point in the workbook we are concentrating on looking for the key information that will later facilitate connections with the inheritance of faith.

Look at these reflections carefully. In each case try to discover how the key issues became apparent. Which tools and techniques have been described in this Unit?

What are you reactions on reading these stories? Try writing the reactions in your journal. Coming back to the reactions in a few days may give you some help on understanding how you confront unpleasant realities in your own life.

Martin's story

Martin found himself in a situation where he was being pulled in two ways very firmly. One side was the need for the business to stay competitive, the other was being aware of the likely effects of action taken to achieve it.

He understood the business issues well. The company could only stay alive and well if it was competitive. Its virtual monopoly was fragile: There was no room for sentiment about such things. It could only remain competitive if there were fewer people working for it.

However he knew the human cost. He had grown up just before the second world war and he knew the effects still felt then of the thirties depression. He knew the cost of unemployment, etched into faces expressing that hopelessness and fear that marked the end of the road. He remembered whole communities in which only mass solidarity in misfortune prevented a breakdown of values and order. He felt that there was something positively unchristian about such situations. Yet his job required he plan for it.

How could he, claiming to be a Christian, promote such devastating action by the company? If outwardly he was pulled two ways he had inward tensions too. He could choose the way of heroic martyrdom expressing his beliefs that people mattered more than money. That would achieve little but disparagement of him and his faith, and would discredit God. A second option seemed to be to massage the figures, keeping a few more hundred people at work but at the continued risk of the whole enterprise failing. This option also put his own job at risk.

As Martin saw it only by keeping his job could he help to bring Christ into the situation. There was no value to God in him being the first on the dole! He could only keep his job if he offered the directors the finest possible advice on reducing staff and developing the 'high-tech base' of the industry. How could he reconcile these conflicting ideals?

The village church story

The Church Council had many problems. It knew it could not deal with the big issues. There were plenty of smaller problems for which it did not have any answers; traffic between the church and the people, the cold clammy

building that laughed with derision at its heating system, the age of the congregation making it older than the local over-60s club, and its image in the community being indescribable. It seemed that for years only the most inflexible of people had dared enter the building.

Gradually the minister put on the agenda the big issues: community hatred and the church's mission. Coming from outside he could see it. From inside it felt as if they were children caught in the act of stealing apples from the neighbour's tree – only much worse. 'What me?' 'Hatred? What hatred?' For a long time the issues were not able to be owned.

Slowly it happened. One person from the village found her heart being softened by what she heard of God's love for her. She responded and found forgiveness. She discovered that she had a role to play by first admitting her feelings for the people on the council estate, and then encouraging others to do so. Over time, one by one, sheepishly and meekly, the church council members found that they could admit their hatred too. They likewise found forgiveness.

With the forgiveness they found they started to pardon the people for living on what had been their green fields. The hatred dissolving, they felt the hurt even greater.

How could they begin to take steps towards mission? Could they move towards all the people who lived in their area whilst such hatred still emanated from the village? At least the twin big problems were now owned.

Paul's story

Paul was very uneasy about the likelihood of war. It was one thing to join the army to defend one's own country against an aggressive communist regime, especially if the likelihood of war was small in the presence of great vigilance. It was another to fight in a conflict that might only be about the economics of oil.

Paul knew that he was not a pacifist. He had been required to stand up to others plenty of times and was prepared to do so again. He knew that situations where right was on one side only were rare. This fight was being portrayed by the politicians as between totally good and absolute evil. That was taking things too far. This war might be justified, but it was unlikely to be totally just.

The more he thought about it the closer this conflict came to being the 'just war' of Christian theology. He could not be wholly sure.

There was a second key issue. There is a saying that 'Life's a bitch and then you die.' Paul heard this almost as the motto of some soldiers. For him, as a Christian, this could not be true. He believed that in all the apparent ghastliness of life there was hope. He knew he should try to stand by those who felt hopelessness and point them to Jesus. Christ alone could bring hope for this world and the next.

On page 46, I asked you to write the first stage of three reflections on issues in the wider world. Now you should write the second stage of each of them, trying to formulate what is the *significant information* and which are the *key issues*. You should aim for 300 to 500 words for each of the three. This will take you some time and you should not go on to the next Unit until you have completed it.

It may be that reflections like these are unfamiliar. Although some of us are used to being reflective about our personal lives, few people are reflective about the social, political and economic situations that surround them. You may find that you have to work quite hard at first to do this exercise.

Unit 6

TOWARDS COMPETENCE

CONTENTS

PURPOSE

The purpose of this Unit is to help you find the most appropriate kinds of connections between your experience and Christian faith, and so increase your competence in theological reflection.

EXAMINING THE FIT

In this Unit we shall be thinking about how to make the appropriate connections between our experience and our 'inheritance of faith'. There will always be *some* connections, if we work hard at finding them. What is more difficult is to find the connection that really fits. It is a little like finding the right spanner to turn a nut. At first sight the wrong spanner may look about right, and even if it is a little too large it might turn the nut at first. But only if it is right will it be able to screw the nut up tight.

The crucial part of theological reflection is being able to find a satisfactory connection between the experience and the 'inheritance of faith'. When we start with our experience we need to identify things from the bible and the church's life that have some connections with that experience. Then we have to examine all of these things to find which intermeshes with our experience *best*.

Two dimensions

Whilst we are doing this we can expect that there are two dimensions to our activity. One dimension is our *intellect*. We will be using all our brain power to do this work. The other dimension is the *spiritual*. Whilst we engage with our mind we look for the Spirit's work of leading us into all truth. At this point in the process there is often the need for the real creativity that is the Spirit's hallmark.

Usually we start tentatively, even if there is something which has that 'eureka' quality about it. As the process continues we can expect to have continually greater insight. If we are getting it wrong we might intuitively sense this, even if we are not able to discern why – another aspect of the Spirit's work.

Two stories

What we are looking for are two 'stories' in parallel, one from experience and one from the 'inheritance of faith'. Your mind can then move between the two, concentrating first on one and then the other, noting how they fit together. As your mind oscillates between them you will recognise the similarities and the differences. If they fit well then, as you examine each side, your insight will grow and there will be new things to learn.

Two examples

Imagine for a moment that you are a volunteer worker in a major charity. As you gain greater experience of the charity you find that all is not well. It is not that there are downright lies told. It is that the plain truth is avoided. You want to know how to behave in this situation, so you look for parallels in the scriptures. You search for situations where the truth is not told.

Amongst many others you would find:
- Adam and Eve in the garden (Genesis 3)
- Cain quizzed about Abel (Genesis 4)
- The defeat at Ai after contraband had been hidden (Joshua 7)
- Solomon not following the way of David (1 Kings 11)
- False measures of weight (Amos 8:5)
- Herod and the Magi (Matthew 2)
- Annanias and Sapphira (Acts 5)
- Peter and the Jewish Christians in Antioch (Galatians 2:11)

On looking closely at these you recognise that in some there is deliberate deception, and in others truth is fudged in an attempt to keep peace with all. The latter seems to be nearer the reality of the situation you face, and so you look more closely at the two where this is the case – Solomon and Peter.

Either of these could well fit the situation and be helpful. In both we would note that, unchallenged and unchanged, the situation would inexorably lead to greater difficulties. In the case of Solomon this was the outcome. In the case of Peter the reality was challenged by Paul, with fairly contentious results.

This might lead us to conclude that although we can recognise the situation we do not feel able to make a challenge until we are well supported. Or we may feel that we can make comment despite our own position being vulnerable.

For another example we can take the case of belonging to a church which is at some sort of crossroads. Taken one way the future looks positive. Other decisions may bring about decline. If the choice to go for the positive is taken, there will have to be great change and there will be problems to solve. Many people may not be willing to go that way.

We might note the following as possible biblical parallels:
- Abraham leaving Ur (Genesis 12)
- The Israelites in terror by the Red Sea (Ex. 14:10)
- The Israelites afraid having heard the twelve spies' report (Numbers 14)
- Josiah and his reforms of worship (2 Kings 22)
- Ezekiel challenged to give encouragement to the exiles (Ezekiel 2)
- Jonah being asked to preach in Nineveh (Jonah 1)
- The disciples asked to feed five thousand (Mark 6:36)
- Peter trying to persuade after visiting Cornelius (Acts 11:2)
- Paul trying to rehabilitate Onesimus (Philemon)

We might note other examples from our knowledge of church history. Having found all these examples you might look again at your situation and note that it is not primarily about worship or devotion but more about shrinking away from the overwhelming needs. You might then decide that it was nearer the Israelites afraid having heard the twelve spies' report and the disciples asked to feed five thousand.

Either of these might make a good parallel and be worth pursuing to see if one fits better than the other. Given the warning in the Old Testament passage you might want to ask the church to be clearer on what the opportunities and difficulties are. From there you might encourage them to see God's hand in it and that the future is worth fighting for.

Getting the *wrong* connections can be a problem. The old story comes to mind of the person who, whenever he wanted guidance, blindly took a pin and pointed to the scriptures. This was soon found to be wanting when one day he pointed to 'Judas went and hanged himself', and immediately afterwards 'Go and do thou likewise'!!

Two dangers

When we are trying to sort our what fits we are in twofold danger.

The first is that we will try to make fit whatever will lead in the direction we want. Creative links are particularly vulnerable to this because they are often sensed intuitively rather than worked out by logic. So it can be harder to pinpoint the inconsistency, and see the choice of 'fit' for what it is – justifying what we want.

The second is that when we recognise the likely outcome of our reflection and perceive what we might be asked to do, we are afraid of the consequences of this action and are tempted to ensure our reflection points elsewhere. It is said that when Nelson wanted to avoid seeing the enemy's strength, for fear it would dent his courage, he put his telescope to his blind eye. We are all capable of the same avoidance.

HOW HARD SHOULD YOU TRY?

There is plenty of advice in the book of Proverbs about not being lazy. This is followed up by a Christian tradition of diligence. The question sometimes comes 'How hard should I work?' A quick look at the Bible might give you two views.

√ Looking for scriptural parallels you might note the parable of the talents (Matt 25:14), the illustration about the runner at the races (1 Cor 9:24), and Paul writing about straining on to the goal (Phil 3:14). Each of these might persuade you that you should neglect everything for work.

√ You might, instead, note the injunctions in Leviticus (e.g. chapter 25) about not taking everything that the land can offer, and the Sermon on the Mount's teaching about not being anxious. These might encourage you to have work in proportion.

If you are engaged in reflection on work, then you have to be careful to choose the right biblical material. If you have a Protestant background, with its strong work ethic, it might lure you unwittingly into solely concentrating on the first view. You will need to understand the scripture well enough to know that Paul was not talking about work but about his desire to know Christ more fully. Theological reflection on work starting from the first view is likely to be flawed.

CONFIDENCE IN DIVERSITY

Having thought about how we make the appropriate connections between our experience and our inheritance of faith, we now need to consider how we can be confident we have the *best* connection.

This is especially important if we have to take significant action on the basis of the results of our reflection. On one course I was directing more than half the members (eight out of fifteen) decided to change jobs as a result of thinking more about their lives. None of the staff on the course even mentioned changing jobs, but individual members on the course, through their theological reflection, had independently decided that major change was necessary.

If our reflection is to have such serious consequences we have to be sure we are getting it right – or not getting it far wrong. We might like to think we can check all the likely biblical parallels. My bible has more than a thousand pages and a cursory read would take weeks. We would have to check carefully though two thousand years of church history. There are millions who have served Christ in their own generations who have stories to tell of faithfulness in the face of an unbelieving world.

REVIEW

Can you remember the two dangers in trying to get the fit right, from the previous page?

There are several tests we can apply. None will ensure we are right (the spiritual life is never risk free), but they can help us check it out. We will need to ensure that our two accounts do fit each other – not that they will fit at every point, but there will be salient and significant points where they do. We have to remember too that the 'fit' at the *significant* points is the most important. That is why we have taken such a great deal of time to note the significant issues.

Testing for confidence

If we are to help ourselves to be more confident then we have to ensure:

- **we have examined ourselves about whether we have any predisposition to choose one theme rather than another. If we have then our own judgement may be somewhat skewed.**
- **we have considered carefully the view of others who have thought about our reflection. These need to be people whom we can trust and who are prepared to tell us if they think we are wrong.**
- **we have reworked our reflection in the light of the whole essence and spirit of the scriptures. If a quotation is out of context, or an interpretation is not substantiated by the rest of scripture, we have to exercise great caution.**
- **we have asked whether this is one of our 'favourite' themes. A preacher I know delivers very similar sermons whatever the text; and some people in their theological reflection can relate everything to the Sermon on the Mount!**

Many-eyed truth

We have also to note that as Christians from the Western Protestant tradition we tend to think that there will be only one true view. We have grown up in world view where truth is 'single eyed'. This is unfortunate because truth is 'many eyed'. In all theological studies, including reflection, we have to come to terms with the scriptures being 'many eyed'.

Sometimes things seem to be in stark contrast to each other. This is true, for example, of the relationship of the person to the state. This will come up inevitably in theological reflection from time to time, as we think of social policy, war, judicial matters or taxation. Put at its simplest, and without many of the qualifications one would wish to make in a scholarly article, there seem to be two very different views in scripture.

View 1

The view we are more familiar with is of the state instituted by God and perceived to be benign. One might cite Jesus' teaching that we are to render unto Caesar the things that are Caesar's. One could also point to Paul in Romans 13, 'For government, a terror to crime, has no terrors for good behaviour.'

View 2

However, one must not neglect the views of the writer of Daniel. One would hardly imagine that after the lion's den and the burning, fiery furnace, he could have said that there were no terrors for good behaviour! More explicitly one reads John in Revelation 14 – 18 using the term 'Babylon' as a covert name for Rome, and describing it in the most lurid terms especially in relation to its godlessness.

When we are engaged in theological reflection we have to note that although we would like scripture to be 'single eyed' it is not. This means we have to be extra careful in the presence of alternative viewpoints.

Towards a harmony

Scripture teaches the same lessons through different media. We find that narrative, letters, gospels, prophecy, can all give the same message though with different nuances. Each of us will find one style easier to encompass than another. Each perspective adds something to the others, and we may need to use more than one viewpoint if we are to gain a fuller understanding. Where there are differing perspectives we can hold them in parallel.

There is a theme in the scriptures of **leaving all that is dear**, of all that is secure in finance, affection and belief, and travelling in pilgrimage:
- ◆ Abraham was asked to leave his father's house (Gen 12).
- ◆ The children of Israel left Egypt.
- ◆ Jesus taught, 'If anyone comes to me and does not hate his father and mother… he cannot be a disciple of mine' (Luke 14:26).
- ◆ Paul wrestled with his call to preach to the gentiles whilst his own people were blind to the gospel and indeed persecuted him for his efforts (Romans 9-11).

Each image (and there are more in the scriptures) gives a different angle on 'leaving home'. Together they produce a compelling call.

LEAVING

Who else left 'home'? You might like to start a list with Jonah and Ruth who left their physical homes, adding those who left other securities.

I hope you have been noticing that undertaking the process of theological reflection requires quite a lot of knowledge about the Bible and theology. Part of the process of improving your ability in theological reflection includes increasing your knowledge of theology and the Bible. How could you go about this?

5 SECURITY CHECKS FOR GOOD REFLECTION

When travelling to Israel by air using an El Al flight you can expect to be subject to a very long period of time between checking-in at the airport and boarding the plane. There are numerous checks on baggage and many questions to be answered. In resigning yourself to having to be patient, it is a help to know that the result is a flight safe from terrorists.

When we know the long term value of something that includes temporary inconvenience, we are more prepared to accept the discomfort with understanding. There are some 'inconveniences' associated with good theological reflection that we will be better able to handle if we understand them. They will help to keep us and those around us safe as we undertake the theological reflection journey.

We can help ourselves in five ways. I have already hinted at them and now they can be expanded.

At peace with uncertainty

Most of us like feeling secure. Our image of the 'good life' is of stability in our finance, relationships, home, church and work.

There is another side to life which can also feel good – uncertainty. Perhaps you have tried rock climbing and felt that buzz that comes from dangling over a long drop supported by your fingers and toes and protected by only a rope. To some people it is hell! But this controlled uncertainty brings the stress that is creative. You learn how to do it better, gaining a greater degree of skill or finding a better route. Without stress of that nature there is little growth and little progress.

If you are to be engaged in theological reflection, you will discover that it has its uncertainties. What will this lead to? Have I got the right answer? (There are no correct answer pages at the back of this workbook!) Those uncertainties bring stress – but the sort of stress that can be creative. We can content ourselves with it if we hold on to the fact that without it there will be no real growth.

In supportive surroundings

This workbook asks some very awkward questions. It poses some disturbing issues. It offers uncomfortable information. If you are coping with this on your own you will find it hard. This is

I recently bought a greenhouse. It arrived from the manufacturers in large units (six pieces of wall, a door, six pieces for the roof). Laying the foundations was no problem. However when the exciting day came to erect it I knew it would be unsafe until all the major pieces were in place. In my anxiety to erect it before some expected bad weather arrived I put up several pieces 'inside out'. They had to be taken down before beginning again. The anxiety and stress remained until all the structure was up and safe.

What experiences have you of doing something that cannot be left until complete or safe?

why I believe you need a mentor. However you may need more help than that.

You will need to ask yourself which parts of your surroundings are being helpful to this process and which are not. Parts of your surroundings (e.g. family, leisure groups) may be supportive and sympathetic to your journey. Others (e.g. work, church) may be apathetic and some even downright hostile.

I encourage you to assess your surroundings accurately and recognise their influence on you for good or ill. You may have to come to terms with the fact that certain parts cannot and will not be supportive to this venture, and that within them you are unable to share this part of your story. This will give you greater incentive to re-evaluate the parts that *are* helpful, and place your weight on them.

Not driven by cherished beliefs

All of us have our cherished doctrines, beliefs and stories. They are familiar friends like the ornaments on the mantelpiece. They give us meaning, purpose and stability in a rapidly changing environment.

Some have value out of proportion to their intrinsic worth. Most parents will tell you of the occasions when they have tidied the mess their children have left behind, only to discover later that amongst the litter now in the dustbin was a scrap of paper which was a highly treasured possession.

We all intuitively value our cherished opinions and compulsively rush to their defence. If you are to gain greater insight and do better theological reflection, you will need to become aware of times when you are defending these viewpoints. As your awareness grows you will be able to suspend your defences temporarily and allow something new.

Creating new pigeonholes

Even the most disorganised of us has a mental filing cabinet in which we store experiences and information. Just like a filing system it comprises various categories – experiences of loss, times of joy, how I handle other people's anger, bible passages I cling to, scripture verses I avoid. Every day we file the happenings into their various categories. When something happens that doesn't fit one of these categories we tend either to lever it into one that it does not quite fit, or to file it in the waste paper basket entitled 'trying to forget'.

As you engage in theological reflection you will regularly be faced with things that do not fit. Rather than try to pigeonhole them inappropriately or forget them, you need to be open to the fact that it is new – and open a 'file' for it with a new label. As time goes by you may find you have several of these new files, each causing you some distress because your mind is trying to lever each into an existing 'file'. You have to let these new things just 'be' until the new files are accepted as part of the system.

Refining the motivation

The source of your motivation has a direct effect on your ability to learn (see pp 6-7). it is important, when dealing with these more difficult parts of theological reflection, that you hold in the forefront of your mind that you want to learn this for your own growth. If your motivation is 'I'm learning this because I'm told to' this may not give you enough support when it all feels too stressful.

If you feel your motivation is waning, you may need to identify again the reasons why you are doing this study. Concentrate particularly on the ones that are most like
♦   'Because I want to understand God more.'
♦   'Because I wish to interpret my experience more.'
♦   'Because I need to have my life a unified whole and not compartmentalised into "faith" and "the rest".'

'We know that suffering trains us to endure, and endurance brings proof that we have stood the test, and this proof is the ground of hope.'
(Romans 5:3)

FACING THE THEOLOGICAL SLOG

Football match crowds can be very cruel. I am not thinking of violence. Nor even verbal abuse. I am remembering the taunts, jeers and songs that put down the opposition. A favourite one from the supporters of the team in the lead is to chant 'Easy, Easy, Easy.' To the perspiring players on the losing side who are playing for all their worth, this is a grave insult!

Most jobs in the hands of an expert do look easy. They may be complex, and if we actually try them they seem impossible, but in the hands of a person of experience and expertise nothing may seem simpler.

There is no doubt that at this stage of your learning, when you try theological reflection it will appear to be a major effort. This is to be expected with anything new. There is an added factor here which can make it difficult even for those who are used to the hard slog of learning – you are wrestling not only intellectually but spiritually.

Hard on the mind

Henri Nouwen said of theological reflection that it 'requires the application of our will power in a concentrated effort; it calls for discipline, endurance, patience and much mental effort.'

There is no alternative to this. You need to look at the issues, think about them, wrestle with them, turn mental somersaults, look at them from every conceivable angle, put them down, take them up, have insights in the middle of the night or in the bath – and perpetually carry a notebook.

It may require talking about it with a friend until they are bored with it and they only continue to listen for the friendship's sake. It may mean losing some people from your circle of friends (at least temporarily) because they do not want to be contaminated with the questions you are asking.

This is not true just of theological reflection. Educational research shows that good learning usually requires this sort of wrestling. If you study theology at college or university you will have to face questions about the Incarnation and the Trinity. You may scrape a pass by quoting the ancient and modern authorities on the subject. But if you really want to understand what the arguments are all about, you will need to put in this sort of mental effort. It is the same for anyone who wants to understand the complexities of almost anything, from building good bridges to delving inside the mind of a great politician.

Hard on the soul

Even when you have learnt to focus your mind and your concentration there is a further factor you have to consider. There are spiritual issues that stand alongside the mental ones.

In John 5 we read of a crippled man who was amongst a crowd of other disabled people by the pool of Bethesda. He had good reason never to be first when the water was disturbed. Jesus asked him, 'Do you want to recover?' There must have been some doubt in Jesus' mind that the man wanted to be well. Did he want to take responsibility for having a normal life with job, wife, children, housing, choices? Perhaps all he wanted was to live depressed, sitting by the pool in the company of others, and existing on charity. Jesus was not in the business of healing people who did not wish to face the opportunities and struggles of a new life.

> **Perhaps you could replace Jesus' question with one to you. 'Do you *want* deep Christian insight into life?'**

There are parallels with the act of fasting. God gave us all the good things of life to enjoy, so intrinsically there is no great merit in going without food. The significance is in the intention, carried through into the uncomfortable action. By fasting I am saying I want something enough to go without breakfast and lunch, to spend time in prayer, even to beat on the doors of heaven if necessary. Do you want this deep insight enough to make sacrifices for it?

If you want insight into the truth about God's world then it is important for you to be sure you desire it. Do you want it even if it will upset your plans, hopes, and comfort? Before the Spirit will impart the insight you request, He wishes you to be sure you are ready to bear the consequences. Are you aware that when once you understand more deeply, something in your life may have to change quite radically?

You may remember James and John wanting to be on the right and left of Jesus in His kingdom and not understanding the significance of what they were asking. All he could promise them was the opportunity to share his sufferings. Are you prepared to wrestle with the answers to your reflections to the point of taking risky action? Or do you just want the insight of the armchair critic? It may be that the insight the Spirit wants to give is too important to be treated that way.

Once you are sure that you do want to understand, then you can rest on the promise that 'to those who ask it will be given'.

> **'Beg for knowledge; plead for insight. Look for it as hard as you would for silver or some hidden treasure.'**
> Proverbs 2:3-4

WELLBEING – FEELING OR REALITY?

I once prayed to be relieved of consistent headaches that were a great burden. I had suffered with them for twenty five years. Why did I get them? What was the point? Was I not trying to live in God's way? Slowly I was made aware that I received much satisfaction through working hard. I received good 'vibes' from living in the fast lane of ministry. The insight given caused me to have to choose between feeling good because so much was being achieved and the possibility (no more) that some of the headaches may go.

Are there issues about which you have written, where some deeper insight may cause very unwelcome change?

PROVERBS

The book of Proverbs contrasts the easy life of foolishness leading to destruction, with hard won wisdom that starts with the 'fear of the Lord'. Proverbs 2 is worth meditating upon at this point.

PERSONAL STORIES: 3

In this Unit we have been examining connections, and the effort needed to facilitate them. The next stage in the stories shows this. Since they are, like the rest of the examples in this workbook, real events, the parallels are not perfect. You may have to make a few mental and spiritual leaps yourself as you read.

CONNECTIONS

These pages illustrate
- the right choice of connections
- the need for effort and application
- the difficulties of holding on through the process

From the information given, are there other connections that could have been made? If someone came to you with any one of these stories, what would you imagine might happen to them next?

Alison

When reading the Old Testament, especially looking at the prophets e.g. 1 Kings 19 – God saying to Elijah 'Why are you here?' and God speaking not in the noise but in the quiet, causing Elijah to hide his face; it became evident to me that God was saying that to me too, and calling me into places where I could not do His will in my own strength. Looking at the story of David, I realised that God could use me, a sinner, I did not have to be perfect in order to be used by God. He could take my past, my power, my being in control, and use it for His purposes, once I had relinquished it.

The words of Moses in Exodus 4.13 'Lord send anyone else you like' became very familiar to me as I wrestled with what God was asking of me. It became obvious to me that I had to take up the new post and then God would show me that I could rely on His power and not my own.

I needed help at this time to untangle my own feelings about the past, for not only was I being asked to move jobs, but God was also calling me into new areas of work within the Parish, where the use of my own power would be totally wrong. I had to spend a considerable period of time with a counsellor, to help me to actually face the past, to relate that past out loud, to own it and seek forgiveness. This talking with another, made me feel utterly vulnerable, and for the first time for many years, I wept on numerous occasions.

Go back to your reflections begun in Unit 3 and continued in Unit 5. You are to begin the process of making your own connections for your reflections. Search for something that makes the appropriate connections and start writing it out like the ones on these pages. You should use 300 – 500 words each.

You may well find that the effort involved in continuing to reflect on all three reflections is just too much. That is understandable – theological reflection is hard work. You may also find that some reflections seem to be 'disappearing' on you, as they turn out to be not what they at first seemed.

If so, drop one of the reflections now. It is important to keep two up, so that later in the workbook you have a choice about which to see through to completion!

Tony and Jayne

Jayne and I became aware that God acts as a shepherd. It came first in a sermon but then there were successive events which called it to mind. It was pointed out to me that a good shepherd moves his sheep from the pasture on which they have been grazed to a field with new grass. The sheep may feel that there is nothing to be gained by going but the shepherd knows the state of the fields, both old and new, and can use his judgement to decide the best time to move them on.

The second truth that we came to realise was that sheep are better shorn than left with an over-grown and burdensome coat. They are fleeced for their wool in an operation that the sheep certainly does not appreciate and to which it strongly objects. For some time after they seem to feel the cold. Yet without the annual shearing the coat would matt, becoming far too heavy for the sheep, and harbouring even more of the ticks and other parasites that makes the sheep uncomfortable. Shearing releases the sheep for renewed friskiness.

We began to recognise that we were being called to move on, and that it would involve considerable loss through 'shearing'. At first we thought this meant that we should move churches. Forays in that direction proved that this was not a sufficient move. Moving job and house might be enough but our attempts seemed not to have God's call on them. Eventually we recognised that the call was for me to retire, and for us to move district and move to a church that seemed more in tune with our understanding of the gospel.

Going away also would be of significance for relations with our elder son. Though welcome he would no longer be able to call and feel the new home 'his'. This might also free Jayne from feeling that she was duty bound to care for him whatever ill he did to her.

IS BETTER WORSE?

I was recently mending the vacuum cleaner. The switch had broken. Into it went four wires. To mend it required all four wires to be put into the right places in the new switch. The wrong connections may have caused it not to work, or to fuse the system, or to cause something worse! One pair wrong and one pair right may have been more serious than all of them wrong…

Sarah

I spent a day at a local church where the visiting speaker based his study on the passage from John 15 about the Vine. Among other things he spoke of the deep pain and loss sometimes experienced during radical pruning, but how vital it was for new and healthy growth, sometimes crucial for life itself.

The speaker was from America and had many unexpected and interesting ways of illustrating his message. He included the pruning of unhealthy and spoilt relationships, saying how we must sometimes have the courage to face the truth of damaging or dead branches, letting people go, actually cutting them out of our lives.

If I took action towards a divorce there would be pruning, drastic pruning that would be as final as a surgeon's knife. There would be no anaesthetic. It would be like elective surgery, rather than crisis intervention. I knew I could make that choice, and underneath I was quietly aware that it would bring cleansing like any good pruning. There would be the healing nature of the action although nothing would ease the pain.

WORLD STORIES: 3

In this Unit we have been thinking about the connections between experience and 'faith'. You have been considering how best to assure yourself that your reflections are a good fit.

In this episode of the stories we see how this worked out for others.

Martin's story

Martin began to think carefully about a Christian understanding of this situation he faced. The gospels might seem to have little in them about such complex situations but he tried to take note of what he could glean. He began to note that Jesus ministered in a complex economic and political situation. There was an occupying power. There were hypocritical political leaders hoping both to work with the Romans so as to partake in the devolved power  and also demanding that they should not rule. There were economic consequences. Some profited from the occupation, some lost out. The gospels seem to record little, but the tensions came out in the question 'Should we pay taxes to Caesar?' Jesus's answer gave a strong clue to Martin. Render to Caesar and to God their dues. He began to realise that both the company and its workforce had claims on him; one contractual, one moral. He would have to view both needs simultaneously.

The narratives about Jesus' trial show the tensions between different powerful people in stark relief: Pilate frightened of Rome, priestly power masquerading as co-operation, Herod balancing the two. Yet in the midst of the conflict there were people to be cared about. Peter denying Him. Pilate scrabbling for truth. Martin noted that even in the darkest of times there were the opportunities to focus on the needs of people.

Martin realised that he could do little to stop the remorseless tide of world economics, but it did not stop him trying to help those who were to be its victims. He could act to give hope, to communicate that people did matter.

It might be a bit tricky keeping his job in the process. There would be those who believed that the business ended with the balance sheet. He would have to show that wider considerations were also good for the bottom line.

The village church story

Reconciliation costs. There was reconciliation to be attempted so that people could live in peace together. Young people on both sides were beginning to take up stances that could result in conflict between the council estate and the village.

Reconciliation in the bible looked serious. There was Jacob and Esau, Jacob having to return in penitence to the brother he had wronged. The example of Ezekiel living amongst the exiles as a testimony that God had not forgotten them, was not lost on the Council. At the Incarnation the angels proclaimed peace on earth. The cross was the symbol of reconciliation.

If the church was to be reconciling community in the midst of two communities in conflict, it had to be *with* both of them, holding them together. The church's mission to those communities must first be a proclamation of reconciliation. How could it? The members had only just become reconciled to the idea of other people in its area. Yet they knew that without that reconciliation they had nothing to say except platitudes.

If they could act as a reconciling community then they would have something to say, not just about the two or three communities, but also about a God who reconciles people to himself. The very heart of the Christian faith travelled the same journey.

Clues from family history

The individuals in families often bear a considerable resemblance to each other. 'You look just like your mother.' The facial similarity is carried in the genes. There are other resemblances: attitudes, behaviour patterns and medical history that are part genetic and part social.

If we have family in the USA we might say, 'We have connections in the States.' This meaning of the word 'connections' links with our use of it.

When we are involved in theological reflection we are looking at a family of situations, then and now. The family history gives clues to the present family issues.

Paul's story

If this was a 'just war' then there was no question that Paul could, and should, join in. He had often studied the campaigns of the Old Testament as Joshua and the people fought their way from the Jordan. They saw the walls of Jericho fall down and fought their way into the hills. They then turned north until they burnt Hazor to the ground. It seemed to Paul that this successful invasion had little sense of fairness for the previous residents of the land – what had they done wrong?

He knew that fairness in human terms is not the same as the justice of God. That is on a different plane. God had regarded that invasion as right, so wars to bring justice might seem to have greater justification.

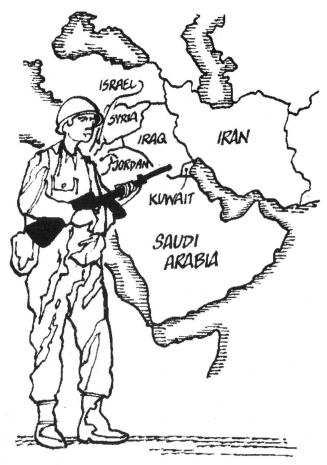

There seemed to be justice on the side of the residents of Kuwait, who has been conquered. There seemed to be real fear of an invasion of Saudi Arabia. There was some expectation that if this was a success then Iraqi attention would turn to cajoling the other Arab states into a holy war against Israel. The official position of the Iraqi's was known to be that the other Arab nations were not being tough enough in their opposition to the state of Israel.

Paul knew that to stand up to such aggression required the toughest of stances and the most resolute defence. Once it was clear that this seemed to be a 'just war' Paul felt able to fight it.

Knowing the awful consequences of war, Paul began to hope for a political settlement in which, under the United Nations threats, the Iraqi forces would withdraw. He could pray for that too. However he knew that to withdraw would cause a loss of face to the Iraqi rulers and they would lose all credibility amongst other rulers in the region. That was very unlikely. A war was immanent and he would have to join in.

Now go back to your reflections on the wider world begun in Unit 3 and continued in Unit 5. You are to begin the process of making your own connections for your reflections. Search for something that makes the appropriate connections and start writing it out like the ones on these pages. You should use 300 – 500 words each.

Again you may need to make a choice and focus on two of the three reflections. But make sure you keep up two of them at this stage in the workbook.

Unit 7

REVISITING THE STORY

PURPOSE

The purpose of this Unit is to enable you to revise your interpretation of your experience in the light of your Christian reflection.

DO IT AGAIN!

REVISIONISM

In Marxist politics there is a process through which the past is rethought. It is known as revisionism. In this the history is retold, changing the facts, influences and persons to fit in with current political ideology. Often the baddies become the goodies and vice versa. This opens the way for the prosecution of past leaders and total changes in the whole fabric of society. The result can be so grossly false that those who lived through the period are unable to recognise the new story from their experience. People reach the position where it is hardly possible for them to tell which version is 'true'.

In this Unit we will be re-writing our stories. In re-writing we are not doing a kind of revisionism. We are not changing facts. (That, if you remember, is one good reason for writing them down at the time). We are changing the interpretation and understanding. We are seeing events and people through new lenses.

This may mean that others who have not taken the opportunity to think about issues deeply are left with a very different, and to us an inadequate, understanding. We have to live with this because we are not in the business of trying to get them to change their views when they do not want to.

An OT equivalent

In the Old Testament from Exodus to Joshua we have an account of what happened as the Israelites escaped from Egypt. For a few minutes, imagine that you are living in Egypt a generation later and have been asked to write an official account of those days.

The story you have grown up with is simple. There was a bunch of foreign slaves who had a radical criminal leader. Despite being well fed and clothed they revolted. Their ploy was to demand their religious rights so they could stop work and go into the desert to pray. Pharaoh gave them leave. When he discovered that they had taken their families and were fleeing, he realised he had been tricked. He took a few of his best military men and chased them. Despite being outnumbered they heroically chased after them even into the sea. In the end justice prevailed because for a generation the escapees roamed around the Sinai desert with nowhere to live.

To check the story's details you travel to meet Joshua after the battle for the land was won. The story they tell is so different that it almost makes no sense at first. You learn to tell it their way too. On returning to Egypt you recognise that nothing can be told of their story if you are to keep your employment. But you wonder for ever whether theirs fits the facts better.

SO FAR...

√ Units 1 and 2 invited you to identify theological reflection, uncovered some of what you already knew and invited you to think about aspects of yourself and God.

√ In Unit 3 you worked on writing up your experience of life.

√ Unit 4 considered our inheritance of faith.

√ Unit 5 reminded us that we needed to identify the significant data, and gave you some tools for finding it.

√ Unit 6 discussed the right connections between your experience and the story of Christian faith.

√ In this Unit we shall be thinking and working on a rewrite of what we uncovered in Unit 3 and thought about in Units 5 and 6.

Reworking and rewriting

As you re-work your story new perceptions will emerge all the time. The story itself may change from being something static – it may become more dynamic as it unfolds the heart of the truth. Wider connections will emerge, deeper analysis will be made.

If you have started from your experience, this new story is likely to have a much greater sense of God's action in it. He is perceived as having a view, taking action, being supportive and strengthening. Divine judgement comes into play. The story takes on a much better balance of things earthly and heavenly. Connections between this world and God grow continually. You identify when you acted within kingdom values and when you did not.

If you started from the inheritance of faith then your life experiences is likely to take on much more meaning. They are now in colour rather than monochrome. They become sharper, more focused, with a sense of human goodness and failure being written even bolder. Black may become blacker, goodness more endearing. Alternatively there may be no goodies and baddies any more. All people may be seen as having lots of faults and failings. Some people may in this new story be seen in a new light, the demure being a coward, and the retiring wise.

You will need to write this new story down.

You may not wish to because you are not sure enough of this new perception. However you need to hold the new story in your mind, and the best way is to commit it to paper. You will need to talk over the new story with your mentor and maybe with others.

At the moment all we are envisaging is that the 'new' story has in it new perspectives and some potential new ways of living.

To write this story:
- take the connections made in the last Unit and hold on to them
- look for previously unseen perspectives and connections in the past and present
- make as many connections as possible between your story and the biblical one

As you look again at your story, try to:
- review your motives and actions
- examine what God may have been trying to do
- re-examine the motives and actions of others
- revise your ethical/moral/political judgements on it

IS TRUTH BELIEVABLE?

There will be a battle in your mind as to whether this new story is believable. At times it will seem far-fetched. This is a matter of faith. You may have to hold it steadily in the face of other people's realities.

Clinging to new stories is always difficult. C. S. Lewis' book *The Screwtape Letters* contains fictitious letters from a senior to a junior devil. It chronicles the temptations of a person as he becomes a Christian and seeks to hold onto faith. In the first chapter the senior devil, Screwtape, tells how he tempted a person away from faith by inviting him to go into the street and look around him. He suggested that a new Christian's faith would feel unreal against the hustle and bustle of the city. Feeling it unreal the person will be sceptical of it.

Whatever is new in the Christian life, be it conversion or the mature Christian having to revise their understanding of something, this a standard temptation. We are tempted to slide from the feeling of unreality (which is right and proper) to the conviction of unbelief.

REWORKING THE STORY OF SCRIPTURE

In Unit 2 (page 21) I invited you to read the words of Jesus about passing through the eye of a needle. You were to think about it from both the point of view of a rich person and also of a poor person. When, like this, we can take alternative viewpoints on scripture we often gain a new perspective.

The prodigal and others

You might like to read the parable of the prodigal son (Luke 15:11-32) from the perspectives of each of the three participants. In turn, look at it from the viewpoints of the younger son, the elder son and the father.

If you have had a turbulent past, going 'off the rails' at some point, then you may find that the younger son's story resonates with your own. However if you then meditate on the story from the point of view of the elder son you might begin to recognise the attitudes of those who made your own 'homecoming' difficult. You might recognise some who rejected your remorse and effectively chose to avoid the party.

To appreciate the father's attitude you will need to think through the passage with him in the forefront of your mind and heart. You may have echoes in yourself of the father's feelings of powerlessness at the younger son's request to leave, especially if you have a child who has chosen a path in life that you cannot affirm. Some people can testify to that terrible discovery, on the coming home of the younger, that the one who had stayed at home did not really belong either. This may resonate with anyone who has discovered the truth about a loved one who is reluctant to be included.

In reading the story in this way we discover that Jesus may have been implying that these three responses are not just three of many. Perhaps in his wisdom about people he discerned that they were the only three possible responses. Every person is either father, older son or younger son. There are no parts for the onlooker, the mother or any other sons because they all take one or other of these three attitudes.

When we start to read the pages of scripture, not from our usual perspective but from someone else's, we are learning to tell a new story. One of these 'new stories' may become ours too.

READING

An excellent study on the story of the prodigal son can be found in Henri Nouwen's book The Return of the Prodigal Son (DLT, 1992). In it he reflects on the painting of that name by Rembrandt.

New or old?

When we start from the treasures of faith, biblical or historical, we can re-tell the story in a way that brings new meaning and perspectives. These 'new stories' may resonate in us more clearly than those stories we know well. They are not really 'new', for they are as old as the original story. But now the new perspective resonates with us clearly.

Another way of explaining this would be to say that the concrete facts, experienced feelings and recognised attitudes of the story remain the same. What changes is the understanding of the hidden part of the story. The new interpretation reveals:
- the attitudes of the other participants
- different spiritual issues: truth, God's intent and action, opposition forces

You might then like to try to think about some other perspectives on other biblical characters.

Ahab: pagan or abused husband?

You may be familiar with the story of Elijah in his controversy with King Ahab and Queen Jezebel (1 Kings 16:29 - 22:40). We usually read it from the point of view of Elijah and reflect with awe on his courage and fortitude in the face of the power of the king.

Try for a moment to read it from the perspective of Ahab. He is king but feels weak at the side of Jezebel. She calls the shots and he feels unable to say 'no' to her immoral ways. When Ahab comes onto the page, the story-teller invites us to despise him for his weakness. That weakness is usually thought of as a desire to run after other gods.

Instead of taking this viewpoint try to re-run this story in your mind by asking what might have happened if Ahab had dramatically changed his stance after the confrontation on Mount Carmel – if, whilst taking the chariot home with defeat written all over him, he had decided to change to being a faithful worshipper of Yahweh.

In my imagination I envisage the following:

The king would first of all have had to deal with Queen Jezebel. She would have ridiculed Ahab for letting his mind be deviated by Elijah's 'magic'. She would have gone on to refuse to change herself and to oppose any changes the king wished to make. She would continue to undermine his kingship calling him 'weak' in front of all. In the end she may have arranged for her son to depose Ahab.

As you use your imagination to read it in this way, you may gain a new awareness of the pressures to stay with the old, no matter how awful. You may perceive the difficulty of changing things.

However it is also likely that in reading it this way you will begin to ask whether there is anyone in life who becomes 'Jezebel' for you. It may be a person who constantly compromises you by nagging you to do the wrong thing and reproves you for being weak when in your eyes you are showing moral strength. In a relationship which you cannot terminate this is very difficult. The extent of its difficulty may only slowly emerge as you turn this story around in your mind.

Moses: hero or murderer?

We have already looked at the Exodus story from the point of view of an Egyptian. Now try imagining the story of Moses from the burning bush to the Red Sea, not from the usual perspective of a reluctant hero, but with Moses as a runaway murderer. He is fearful of the Egyptian authorities arresting and executing him. He is also aware of his own people's unwillingness to let themselves be led by a criminal.

What difference does it make to your understanding of
♦ his reluctance to follow God's call
♦ Pharaoh's rejection of his authority
♦ the people's lack of trust as they camped by the sea shore

Does any of this relate to occasions when you have been called or led by God?

OTHER PASSAGES

to think about include

☞ The feud between Jacob and Esau from Rebekah's standpoint remembering her involvement (Gen 25:19 – 35:21)
☞ The friendship of David and Jonathan from Jonathan's point of view (1 Sam 16 – 31)
☞ The entrepreneurial wife of Proverbs 31:10ff read by her husband who believes women should be very domesticated
☞ Martha's view of Jesus as he sides with Mary over her desire to listen to him (Luke 10:28)

THE TESTS OF REVISION

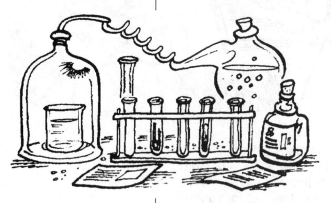

When we write a revised story it opens up a new world. There are new understandings, new connections, new possibilities, and new anxieties. The excitement of new insights is great. The questions soon arise:

♦ Are these new insights true?
♦ Is the new any better than the old?
♦ Have I now a greater grasp of reality?

Before we can answer these we have to know what are the appropriate tools and methods for this sort of testing. We have to bear in mind that we have been well entrenched in another story, we have perhaps built much on it, and we are in many ways committed to it.

Does it fit?

The first test we can apply is to ask the question, 'Does this fit the data I have?' We go back to the original material we wrote. You will remember this material had little interpretation. Re-reading it we can ask, 'Does this interpretation fit the facts, the feelings, the values, the attitudes as experienced at the time?' If we have done our work conscientiously it will, without doubt, fit some. Perhaps it will fit the more significant parts of the data.

The understanding we now have may start turning previously held views upside down. It may well fit the information we gathered very well. Where it does not it will call into question the veracity of the material with which we were working. Sometimes the most significant discoveries in theological reflection are the errors in some of the information we have gathered.

John would have always said he grew up very loved. His home was a model of respectability and all that a child could need seemed to have been provided. He said it, despite a gnawing feeling somewhere in his bones of being unwanted. Later in life, as his own children grew up, he began to think carefully about the past. He remembered that as a child his mother consistently told him that he was loved and cared for. However, the more he thought about it, the more he remembered evidence that did not fit. In fact, quite the opposite.

Most memories of his mother were of someone preoccupied with his father, the other children, her church work and her dog. He noted that quite often he now acted as if he were not wanted, even though he knew himself to be valued and respected at work and at home. In the end, through much heart searching, he had to accept that the evidence was that he was not loved as a child and that his mother had consistently lied to him. It was a terrible struggle to admit eventually what his mother had done, but it freed him to pour out his own love on his family, and in turn to discover the depth of the value they put on him.

Does it work?

A second test we can apply is to answer the question, 'Does this interpretation work?' If it is right, then trying it out will confirm it. We find a way of testing our interpretation. A little different behaviour based on the new understanding can reveal whether we have the truth or not. This is a good way forward to see if our new ideas are grounded in reality.

The church seemed friendly enough. There were people to welcome worshippers. However the new minister was not quite so sure. The welcome only seemed skin deep. The evidence was that some people were very bitter about the past but there was not enough to be sure. So he quietly invited some Christian friends who lived not far away to come and to see how they were greeted. For several weeks they came and all was friendly. One Sunday the person responsible for taking the collection failed to turn up. He asked one or two of the congregation to do it but they declined. The minister then began to recognise something significant – and asked his friend to do the honours. After the service the friend was given the cold shoulder and some very hard stares. This gave the minister the evidence he needed to start questioning whether new worshippers were really welcome.

Is it balanced?

Another test we have to keep in the back of our minds is one we apply to any situation. Does it fit with an understanding of the whole of scripture as well as the passage we are working with? Does any insight of scripture go the other way?

We might reflect that a political leader is going the wrong way and taking the nation down a path of corruption and wickedness. In our 'God thoughts', it might seem to us that God's judgement is upon him and that the time is right for better leadership. We may want to pray earnestly for change, and work for it with all peaceful means. No matter how wicked the situation it is unlikely to be right to attempt to murder the politician in an attempt to remove him…

Is it agreed?

Other people have a part to play in checking out our ideas. Some may be surprised or even shocked at our thoughts. Others may be affirming and encouraging. It is unlikely that everyone will give a positive response. You will need to listen carefully to the responses, distinguishing their feedback to the new story from their concern for you. If everyone is negative about your ideas then you may need to revise them, or recognise that this way forward would be taken without much support.

TWO THINGS STAND OUT

1. We live by faith. There is no such thing as certainty except certainty in God's faithfulness.
2. There will always be loose ends that do not fit.

Given these two caveats, is the 'new' story strong enough to place our weight on?

The apostle Peter was prepared to get out of the boat in the middle of the Sea of Galilee and walk towards Jesus. There may not have been enough faith for him to stay walking but even as he sank he recognised that Jesus could save him. Peter didn't need to sink *or* swim. His 'new story' was good enough to act on – and learn from.

DANGER!
THEOLOGIAN AT WORK

I wonder how you react when you see a DANGER sign? If I see it whilst I am taking a walk along a cliff path contemplating the sea hundreds of feet below and the screaming seagulls wheeling overhead, I may be wise to keep clear of the area and take a detour away from the cliff edge. I would probably take the sign to mean 'Keep well away'.

I do not treat all DANGER signs like that. If I am driving along the road and see a sign with the word DANGER followed by 'flood', 'ice', 'road works', 'no road markings', then I do not immediately plan a diversion. I continue on the planned route but with greatly increased vigilance and much reduced speed. In this case I take it to mean 'Proceed with caution'.

The process of re-writing the story should have the word DANGER printed by it. That word should be understood not as 'Keep well away' but as 'Proceed with caution'. There are at least three hazards.

When you reflect on your life there is the danger of becoming entirely focused on your experience. If you do this you can be left without any objective reference points. Your experience of life may be very subjective. You feel it as if through gloves in which some of the fingers are thickly padded and others have no protection. Misleading parental messages, painful encounters, and cultural values that are questionable may be felt keenly – or not at all. You may be able to describe your experience with great clarity but its connection with objective truth may be seriously corrupted. In the process of re-writing you have to be constantly alert to this danger.

When you re-write your story you can back off from your radical re-interpretations and doubt the new method. You have explored the use of connectivity as well as analysis. You have noted the use of the weaker side of your personality in discovering realities. After making your discovery and formulating the connection between your experience and the treasures of faith, then you can be tempted to revert to your more traditional ways of thinking. You have to proceed with caution through a re-writing process so that you continue to use the new methods that have brought illumination. To set aside immediately what God has used is absurd.

You need to hold in tension both that scripture is authoritative and that you may be reading it through lenses of cultural conditioning that distort its meaning significantly. We have talked about the need for interviewing the text with competence, and that competence over the breadth of theology guarded against simplistic use of the biblical text (pages 52-53). That danger continues to exist as you proceed with the re-writing.

The road ahead

With these cautions in mind re-writing the story can now proceed a little further. Whether you started from the treasures of faith or from your experience, you will soon have a re-written story that interprets the past better. Through your reflection you can now recognise, in both pattern and detail, the resonances between facets of your life and the faith story of the Church.

But re-writing which describes only the past and the present is not complete. As well as looking back and as well as viewing the present, you also have to start looking forward. On the basis of what you know, you need to identify what may happen in the future. You will begin to predict possible future outcomes. You will ask yourself, 'What choices do I now have that will begin to navigate towards the preferred outcome?' These choices and outcomes are based on what you know of God's activity and what you feel confident He would wish to accomplish.

To do this you take the re-written story. You look at the side of it that relates to 'faith'. You note the pattern that evolves beyond the situation as it is now. You ask yourself, 'What would that pattern look like in my situation?' You go on to ask, 'If that happened in my situation, what would it look like? What would I experience?'

In **philosophy** and **mathematics** this process is known as extrapolation. In it people move from what they know to what they might anticipate. The known facts give a pattern. If the pattern is recognised and if it continues one can ask, 'What will happen next?'

In **medicine** the anticipated future course of a disease is known as a prognosis. The doctor has seen several cases like this before. Each had the same conclusion. The prognosis is never certain because there are events that may change the result, but it is a well-informed and educated prediction.

LOOK BACK

Now look back at some of your own reflections. For each ask yourself:

- ☛ What might the patterns suggest as an outcome?
- ☛ What choices do I have and what might be the outcomes of each?
- ☛ Have I the resources actually to make those choices?

Make a few notes for yourself, but do not write anything substantial yet. I will ask you to write when you have worked through the next few pages.

There may be several possible outcomes depending on what you do in the present. Each may set in motion a train of events which as you reflect you may anticipate. You will have to ask yourself some further questions like, 'Which is most right?' and 'Which seems closest to God's heart?'

Some of these reflections may anticipate a future with pain and suffering involved. To choose to set one of these in motion is a significant test of our resolve to be disciples! Some may look very positive with opportunities for further service. Some may seem to have very unpredictable results depending on what others do.

PROPHECY

The word 'prophecy' literally means 'telling forth', 'speaking out' the truth. It is more commonly used to mean 'foretelling' – prediction of the future. When God's prophets spoke, then part of the human thought processes that led them to their predictions perhaps resembled this process of prognosis. Seeing the reality of the situation, they could anticipate God's activity and the results.

For example: A society that finds it hard to be honest with itself may avoid noting innumerable sins. It becomes weak and vulnerable to exploitative leaders who are prepared to be sparing with the truth. The reality becomes progressively harder to discern. When leaders who appeal for a return to truth are prevailed over by those who profit from the unmentionable sins, the point of no return is passed. A prophetic voice may then accurately predict the disintegration of that society.

PERSONAL STORIES: 4

We now continue the three examples that have been running through the workbook. They have previously appeared in Units 3, 5 and 6. You might like to refresh your memory of them before reading on.

In this episode we concentrate on the theme of this Unit – the new story. As you read you may recognise this emerging. There are different emphases in each one.

All these stories involve a 'letting go'. This is a familiar theme in pilgrimage. It corresponds with much biblical material. It fits too with 'putting away other Gods' in the Old Testament, and 'repentance' in the New. The aspect that seems most difficult for us, as God's creatures, is that we have to 'let go' before we can encompass the new. Most of us would like to hold onto the 'past' as security until we are convinced that the new will be all right.

Alison

As I let go of the power, then all sorts of miraculous things began to happen. The story of the new job comes later, but I became a different person. I still had to choose, I could go into situations using power, or without power, having handed my power over to God. He was then in control of it. I had been quite a fearsome person to some, but people began to use me to give them help and to care for them pastorally. God asked me to draw near to someone whom I disliked, and for many years I sat and listened to that person on many occasions. My experiences in the past enabled me to have a sympathetic ear to those who find themselves in similar situations, and not to be judgmental about behaviour and actions.

As I read the scriptures, God started giving me 'pictures', often related to events of the present but sometimes prophetic. I had to learn to share those with others, in order for them to be used. This made me feel very vulnerable but also helped me to recognise what God could do through me for others.

I still need to be reminded that I am a worthy person in the sight of God, it is easy for me to feel guilty that I constantly fail, and if that continued then the power game of protecting myself would also start again. Friends who know me are able to give me words of Scripture, and I seek their prayers at times when I am likely to be in difficult situations. I continue to recognise that I am vulnerable and can only act under Gods' loving care and protection.

Looking back at the previous episodes, write down the shifts of emphases emerging in each account that make each 'a new story'. E.g. Alison's image of moving from 'power' to 'vulnerability'.

Tony and Jayne

Jayne and I started to think about what this new story might be.

The new story would not be of a comfortable home and garden, an uncomfortable church, a demanding job and pain in relationship to our son.

This story was of a new opportunity to move, possibly into a house with an even bigger garden for the plants we loved so much. Leaving those cherished plants too big to take would be a wrench but at least the most prized could be taken. We valued our friends so the question came as to how short a distance we could move and still accomplish all we believed important. The more we thought about it the more it seemed that the distance would have to be over a hundred miles rather than under. We lighted on a town we perceived as appropriate and found a small holiday home to which we could go so that we could begin to make a few contacts. Friends and relations seemed to corroborate the plan, affirming the move.

How I would cope without employment I did not know. I had to test it first by discovering whether early retirement would be acceptable to my employers. I had to think about what I could do, free from having to earn. At this point I discovered that in the town some opportunities for Christian service were opening up that looked really positive.

How about our elder son? God was working within us to help us see that for our protection we had to find a way of distancing ourselves from him. God also showed us that this 'shearing' would be of value to him too. For his own life to be worth anything he had to start to take full responsibility for himself.

After a couple of years in 'dialogue' with this idea of the shepherd who moved and sheared his sheep, we were ready to take the decisive steps.

Sarah

I was given a new understanding of God's grace and mercy, his forgiveness and willingness to become involved in absolutely all the difficulties which we face. This was an enormously personal revelation for me. Somehow I felt that I had been freed to take the step of acknowledging that may marriage had failed.

I came to recognise that the true relationship, the essence of marriage, had ended without any conscious decision on my part. And this revelation was almost like coming out of a thick fog. There was a new clarity of thinking, an awareness of a certain direction that was acceptable and a new door to be opened that actually led somewhere.

Hurt was inevitable with any action, or no action at all, but the moment I had no doubt that with road now being shown to me was offered as the least hurtful way to go. I felt that god had shown his compassion because I had given myself and the whole situation totally to Him, prayed and waited, prayed and waited. It was His moment, his timing.

Making a decision to proceed though the mechanics of divorce felt a purely secular situation. The actual divorce didn't seem such a daunting milestone any more. I felt emotionally and physically released for the overwhelming burden that had been so darkly oppressive for so long. I could let my husband go, even to another woman, and face all the consequences that would inevitably follow.

The 'pruning' would of course remove 'dead wood' but is was incredibly frightening to realise how much I had unwittingly allowed this 'dead wood' to actually prop me up through the later years. I would have to learn new ways to stand up on my own without the familiar restrictions of what had been so damaging, but also as secure as any prison walls.

Now it is time for you to work again on your own reflections that you began in Unit 3. You are to re-tell the story using the insight gained through making the connections of Unit 6. Try writing this down in 300 – 500 words each.

Try to keep up at least two reflections, so you have a choice of which to finish in the next Unit. But you may choose to focus on just one reflection from this point onwards.

WORLD STORIES: 4

We are now re-visiting the stories of those who have been reflecting on issues in the wider world. They are now concentrating on re-telling the story.

It is not only human beings that find new stories. Foxes used to be almost entirely country creatures. They have now learnt that there are good pickings in suburban areas, and are regularly seen in gardens that used to be the preserve of the family cat.

Martin's story

People were to be made redundant in large numbers to secure the continuance of the business. That was obvious and he had the task of putting together the plan that would bring it about. He did it as conscientiously as he could.

He also took advice about what could make the situation positive for the people involved. He resolved to argue that the plans should include:

♦ That the company would be as open as it could be with its employees at all times. There were risks involved with other companies knowing what was planned but they were worth taking. Risks were necessary.

♦ That the company should put into its costs of redundancy not only a good financial package but also real help to re-start people in their own businesses and enterprises. Significant help was key.

♦ That they should begin the process slowly so that they could learn how best to deal with it. Then success stories from those who had been made redundant would be of help to others when their turn came. Hope was a key.

He wanted the company to show its respect for those who had been in its employ, some for many years. In showing and giving that honour it would assist those people to continue to respect themselves as time went on.

He noted that respect, hope, help, and risk were all 'kingdom' values.

The village church story

Light eventually dawned, as it does to those who look for it with heart, mind and soul. One December the heating system in the church was declared inoperative. In desperation the small church community hired the junior school hall for Sunday services. The junior school just happened to be on the council estate.

The worship was warm in temperature and warmed in spirit as the weeks went by. A few people from the estate ventured in and were delighted with their welcome. It felt good and right, despite the villagers being petrified about walking the half mile through the estate on Sunday morning.

Light dawned in the wacky idea that the church was now acting as a reconciling agent. It had crossed the divide. It was no longer just 'them' over there. 'They' had come 'here'. It fitted the biblical patterns well.

As the heating system in the church became usable again the real question arose. Real reconciliation would take years. How could the church be there long enough to do anything useful? Lateral thinking soon suggested the maddest idea of all – a new building. A new building where the two communities met? Or better still, where the three communities met.

Could that building be a church? It could, but what consequences might follow if the church were re-located? What would the villagers say if their building were left unused down its dark and lonely lane? There was sure to be an outcry of pain and feelings of betrayal.

What would one use for money? A small church community could not raise the cost of a new building. Even if they were wealthy it would be impossible, more so since they were poor.

How would the church authorities respond. Could they be persuaded to let it happen?

The idea did not seem sensible, but it did follow biblical patterns and there seemed to be something of God's touch about it. Especially since the basic idea also mopped up most of the smaller issues they had been facing: heating the church, crossing the road, 'them' and 'us'. It even gave the opportunity for appealing more to the under-60s.

> Looking back at the previous episodes, write down the shifts of emphases emerging in each account that make each 'a new story'. E.g. Paul's shift of perception and motivation on deciding the war was justified.

Paul's story

Although he knew he had to join in the war Paul also had the option to remain in Germany. His commanding officer asked him to stay behind as the Welfare Officer, to provide comfort and support to wives and families. Paul believed that his calling was to go with his troops to the battlefield. As a leader, who better to care for them in the forthcoming action?

Caring for them was given a macabre twist when he was reminded that his status as a Reader in the Church meant he was authorised to take funerals. He was given instruction on emergency burial procedures. Now he knew what the deployment might mean – some not coming back. This was for real.

In this new story Paul was going to fight a 'just war'. In a world which often seemed to lack compassion and meaning, he hoped to do something to bring God's justice to bear upon it.

Like everyone else going he would have to leave his wife and family for an indefinite period. They knew that unlike most of the others, he had chosen to go and ignore the safe option of staying with them.

Now it is time for you to work again on your own reflections that you began in Unit 3.

You are to re-tell the story using the insight gained through making the connections of Unit 6. Try writing this down in 300 – 500 words each.

Again, try to keep up two of your world reflections at this stage, so you can choose which to complete in Unit 8. But time and effort may demand that you focus on just one at this point.

Unit 8

ACTIONS
SPEAK
LOUDER

CONTENTS

PURPOSE

The purpose of this Unit is to help you with the final stage of theological reflection – deciding on appropriate action in life, taking it, and reflecting on the results.

DON'T JUST THINK THERE...

We have noted the pattern of theological reflection so far as

- observation
- noting the key issues
- making the connections
- writing the new story

Most of our work has been to understand, to perceive, and to recognise. This Unit is about *taking action*.

As you take action you will find that it corroborates your understanding – or points up its weakness. Either way you will establish the truth of your 'story'. You will also discover more of the ways in which God works with you.

Look again at your journal. Is there something you should *do* about one of the issues you have been reflecting on?

Are there particular ways in which that action will have to be taken, in order to ensure that the action itself has the right values?

Theological reflection is incomplete without it having some effect in our *lives* and in the lives of others. There is a parallel to the words in the Epistle of James: 'Faith without works is dead' (James 2:17).

My Action

The action may be at a *personal* level, sorting out something in our attitudes.

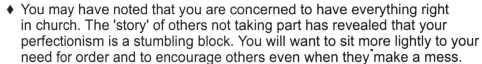

NOT NOW! I'M DOING SOME THEOLOGICAL REFLECTION ON CARING FOR THE LONELY

- ◆ The process of creating the 'new' story may have revealed to you that you are guilty of racism. The right action is repentance.

- ◆ The writing in the last Unit may have uncovered that there is action to be taken at work. You may have discovered that some people are being harassed and that it is within your power to discourage it.

- ◆ You may have noted that you are concerned to have everything right in church. The 'story' of others not taking part has revealed that your perfectionism is a stumbling block. You will want to sit more lightly to your need for order and to encourage others even when they make a mess.

- ◆ Your 'story' may have helped you to realise that your town needs a different voice in its politics. You decide to see if it is possible to stand as an independent candidate at the next election.

Our Action

Some action will have to be *corporate*.

- ◆ A group of young mothers have decided that church life should include a creche, staffed not just by themselves but also by older members of the congregation. The church needs challenging about whether they value children as part of their community – or whether they just tolerate them.

- ◆ Your 'story' involves your neighbour Fred. At 86 he is still very alert but cannot easily get out. It also involves Sue who lives across the road and does his shopping. Together you investigate the local day centre and find that it copes with so many people who are (to say the least) confused, that rational people do not wish to attend. You discover there are others who are in the same predicament, and so with Sue you form a group to organise a transport service so they can visit each other.

Too late to act?

Occasionally, having worked through a theological reflection, it is too late to do what is necessary. There is no waste in this because it is likely that the situation will recur in a different guise.

For instance, you might have had to leave a job well before recognising the realities of the business you were in, and feel that you would now know what God would have wanted you to do there. Even if you can no longer take action, it is important to know what the right action should have been. Then you are ready the next time you experience something similar.

Like Machiavelli?

Changing things, even if you are sure it is at God's bidding, is bound to provoke some reaction in others. The change is not always welcome. Machiavelli, the political commentator of the 16th century (and in popular thought a byword for ruthlessness on behalf of the State) said:

'There is nothing more difficult to carry out, nor more doubtful of success, nor more dangerous to handle, than to initiate a new order of things. For the reformer has enemies in all who profit by the old order and only lukewarm defenders in all those who would profit by the new order. This lukewarmness arises partly from the incredulity of mankind who do not truly believe in anything new until they have had actual experience of it.'

When you come to the point of making changes, with all the opportunities in them, you can also find yourself provoking difficulties. You must be alert to both opportunities and difficulties.

This is the point at which we all learn what it is to be a disciple of Jesus. If we just want the blessings that come from Him, this is the time we will stop.

How to act?

If there is to be any significant action it has to begin *in* you. Before Jesus began his ministry he was led into the wilderness to be tempted. You have to let go of bad motives and unhelpful attitudes. The action that you take will be part of bringing in God's kingdom. The *way* you do it will have to model good practice in the kingdom. **Means and ends must both be appropriate.**

This will challenge the kind of person you are. So if you are a 'no change' personality you will have to confront your own feelings and be prepared for much upheaval. If you are a 'constant change' character you will have to confront your own predisposition to act before thinking.

You can find some of the qualities that accompany Christian action in the parables of Jesus. They include:

- a generous 'seed sowing' with the expectation that there will be much failure as well as success (Luke 8:4ff)
- the avoidance of looking back (Luke 9:52)
- building is only possible with unity (Luke 11:17)
- some things matter more than what we consider 'basic necessities' (Luke12:31)
- building happens here and now (Luke 17:23)
- childlike trust (Luke 18:16)
- bountiful generosity (Luke 18:29)

The issues of 'How is this to be done?' are best addressed by observing in the gospels how *Jesus* did it. Think about each of these qualities and link it with something in Jesus' life where he showed it in action.

My answers in the margin of page 110.

APPROPRIATE ACTION?

Jesus' ministry of bringing in God's kingdom shows us that it may include

- the provision of the necessities of life
- calming the hostile forces of nature
- exposing and challenging economic exploitation
- exposing and challenging religious hypocrisy
- exposing and challenging falsehood
- healing and wholeness for people, communities and nations
- casting out demons
- removal of causes of suffering
- promoting trust rather than fear

BEATITUDES

The Beatitudes (Matthew 5:1-11) give an indication of the value system which Christians should adopt. What they *do* is not governed by what they wish to achieve but by this radical value system.

Write down (in not more than 12 words each) a statement of the meaning of each of the Beatitudes. My wording for the first one (to get you started) would be: 'knowing and showing our need for God'. My answers in the margin of page 110.

... AND THEN THINK AGAIN!

Your action will have changed the situation. When you have attempted to take action, whether it proved successful or not, neither the situation nor you are the same again.

What might have changed?

First of all, and perhaps most important, *you* have changed. Whether you have been 'successful' in your action or 'unsuccessful', there will have been some significant learning.

You have been looking back at your writing and noting how far you travelled in your understanding, attitudes and perceptions. Now think for a short while about what the action has taught you:

All change!
It could be that the action has made any of these changes *in you*:
♦ greater confidence in your ability to understand correctly
♦ greater confidence to try something new
♦ a different experience of what God does when you are willing to play an active part
♦ a clearer idea of what makes it hard for you to take action
♦ a difference of perspective in the light of new connections which have been made

In *your relationships with others* the action may have made any of these changes:
♦ better understanding of how much influence you have
♦ deeper awareness of other people's motives and intentions
♦ more appropriate reactions to others actions and attitudes
♦ gained or lost friends
♦ a sense of solidarity and bonding with a group

In *your relationship with God* the action may have made any of these changes:
♦ a new understanding of how He brings about His kingdom
♦ a deeper sense of corporate and structural sin
♦ a new awareness of how He feels about His world
♦ a better perception of what to pray for
♦ a more keen appreciation of the vulnerability of the incarnation

Back to the beginning?
The first thing you have to do is to identify what really has happened. You may need to talk this over with your mentor before coming to firm conclusions. These you should write down as fully as you can. They will be needed for the next stage of the process. This learning is the basic information for the next cycle of theological reflection. **Having taken action we learn from it.**

You might feel you are beginning the process again from the start. It is not quite that. It is more of a review. In this review you have to decide whether the new learning has effectively changed the information you had at the start. If the connections have proved to be unhelpful, you search for others and try them.

A work example
You may have started the process by considering the relationship with your boss at work. You may have worked through your reflection on the understanding that she is creative and helpful though with one or two blind spots. However, if after deciding to make one or two specific suggestions to improve the efficiency of the operation you

FACING FAILURE
Theological Reflection when our 'action' has failed is a key factor in our maturity as Christians. Can we recognised what went wrong, address the issues and grow through it? If we have to succeed all the time, we will be unable to face suffering for the sake of Christ.

were treated as if you had made a bid for her job, you might want to revise your understanding of her. The new information gathered in the process has changed one of the basic and key issues. You might decide that your reflection had to be based no longer on Nehemiah and a benevolent King Artaxerxes, but on David and an irascible King Saul who felt threatened.

A school example

Tim was faced with an awkward situation. He was the new minister at the church. Because of his position he was elected Chair of Governors at the local church school. A small group of the governors had been there many years and in the first few months he was almost entirely dependent on them for advice and information. He learnt quickly and soon became aware of the various views on the governing body. He was aware too of the staff perceptions and the parents' attitudes.

The head teacher was consistently on sick leave and the whole school was suffering the consequences. Whenever he made enquiries of what should be done the long-standing governors firmly advised that he ignore it. The lack of staff leadership and the concern of the parents meant it could not be ignored for long. His theological reflection suggested that the long-standing governors were properly concerned for the employment rights of the head, and that his rights were as important as anybody's in this situation. One would have to hold people's rights in tension, not denying his in affirming those of the school children. (Compare this with the creation of the first deacons in the church – the apostles ought to preach whilst the widows ought to receive some practical help. Both needs were met.)

Armed with this he initiated a debate on the subject at a meeting of the governors. He hoped that they would agree a letter to be sent to parents outlining the steps being

taken to improve the leadership of the school whilst the absences continued.

The governors would agree no such thing. The majority required the whole issue to be ignored unless the head wanted to leave. However, a chance remark made a colossal difference. Tim overheard an aside that showed up the realities. The long-standing governors had been chiefly responsible for the appointment of the head. At the time of the interviews they had forgotten to make enquiries about his health. Tim recognised that their reluctance to take any action was born of their guilt. He would have to reflect again and differently on the situation in the light of this new information.

Tim went away and reflected on the effects of unacknowledged guilt. He remembered that it causes bad to become worse. (David wanting Bathsheba eventually led to the division of his family and courtiers – 2 Samuel 11-20). With the right understanding and the knowledge of the likely consequences of not addressing the problem he had the courage to ask a direct question at the next meeting which revealed the failure of the appointing governors.

With their guilt acknowledged they were able to address the issue positively. The rights and needs of all involved were affirmed. Good wishes were communicated to the head. The deputy head was encouraged to take full charge whenever the head was away. Paul soon had all the governors, staff and parents working together to assist the school through a difficult time.

VERIFY IT!

In both these cases the wrong information had led to the wrong conclusions. However, taking action had revealed the true situations.

It might be that *your* reflection proves to be accurate in its basic ideas. The action you take has the results you predicted. This will encourage you to continue to hold that re-written story and to pursue the action it suggests.

MEN AND WOMEN DO IT – DIFFERENTLY

This Unit is about action, action which is the response to our thinking. We noted earlier that people think very differently with a range of emphases (see pages 68-69). In the same way our preferred methods of *action* are personal to us. We know certain things work so we stick with them. There are specific types of result we aim for. There are outcomes we know we will be comfortable with.

Personality has much to do with it. For example, some action will involve conflict. People who are not relaxed with strife will seek action that minimises it, both as they act and in the outcome. Those who enjoy a good fight may encourage it. Those who cannot bear to lose will ensure that if there is conflict they win, and if there is no prospect of success they will avoid argument.

Today political correctness is all important. Because of this I hardly dare write that gender has an effect too. In the midst of this hazardous territory, to simplify the issues is dangerous. It can lead to sweeping generalisations that have no reality. However our work is incomplete without some attention being paid to how women and men may differ in their reactions.

Being the same, being different

Gender gives rise to personality differences in human beings. They are on a spectrum, not in two watertight compartments. In that spectrum there is a bias toward each end, men one way and women the other. For our purposes I wish to point out one identifiable experience that leads to one end of this spectrum. You may be aware of others.

As children grow up it more often that the mother has the closer connection with them, especially if the experience of being 'in mother' in the womb is followed by the mother being the primary carer. Children also have the experience of being aware of their sex from very early, and that it is a primary distinguishing mark. Parents will say, 'We have a girl and two boys.'

DON'T YOU CRY TOO – BIG BOYS DON'T CRY!

As they grow up girls know that they are female, the same as their mother. On the other hand boys grow up knowing they are male, different from their mother. They must be separate from her.

READING

The gender issues in this section are covered well in a book by Celia Hahn *Sexual Paradox* (The Pilgrim Press, New York, 1991). She seeks to show how creative use can be made of male-female tensions in the workplace, in personal life and in the local congregation.

ANSWERS

from page 107
My suggestions for short descriptions of the value system of the Beatitudes (Matthew 5: 1-11) are:
- knowing and showing our need for God
- mourning for a lost world and our losses
- gentleness
- a desire to see justice prevail
- mercy (even on God's enemies)
- purity of motives
- delighting in and seeking peace
- a willingness to be persecuted rather than let wrong be done

This can lead women to feel more comfortable with being 'the same as'. They often enjoy and value their connectedness with others. In contrast, most men are uncomfortable with being like the next person and are more at home being separate and distinct from other people.

When we plan and take action for the Kingdom we are under the influence of these 'comfort zones'. We can expect that most men will find it easier to take pioneering action with singleness of mind, action that results in them being identified as different or distinctive. We can expect that most women will be more comfortable with action with others to discover a synthesis that results in agreement and wholeness.

When we plan and take action in consequence of our 'God thoughts', we should bear this in mind. Both the decisions and the operation can be contaminated by unawareness of these natural differences.

> **Whatever the situation, most men will be drawn towards action that generates distance, most women will move towards activity that produces closeness. When we are aware of these differences we can be aware of the temptations they encourage. We will become more conscious of our own predispositions. We will then be able to take account of them in our decisions.**

In the other's shoes

When we thought about personality types, we noted that reading the scriptures from the perspective of a different person could often be helpful. When we are deciding on action it is often helpful to look at the possibilities from the point of view of the other gender. If you are a person who naturally works towards closeness you may find it helpful to think positively in terms of action that creates distinctiveness and separation. If you are a person who thinks naturally in terms of clear divisions then try imagining methods that might result in greater unity.

This can be particularly helpful in corporate reflection and decision-making. A church committee that includes women and men will often find itself trying to choose between action that feels comfortable to the men and that which feels comfortable to the women. In this case the key people to hear are those who are suggesting action outside their natural dispositions. They may not be right, but their viewpoint is often of great value in finding a way forward that does not come down heavily on either side of the balance.

> ## A TALE OF TWO CHURCHES
> Two churches were trying to work together in the same village. Both had plenty of rhetoric about ecumenism and unity. However the (male) minister of the smaller congregation was primarily concerned about the survival of his church. In consequence he made a virtue of the distinctiveness of their theology and practice, with good results in terms of gentle growth.
>
> The larger church tried to make overtures but each time the smaller one was felt to be making a yet more distinctive statement in response. Aware of the potential damage if this pattern continued, the leadership of the larger church decided it must bide its time, hoping that the growing confidence of survival in the smaller church would change their reactions. However they reckoned without several women of the larger congregation who decided there must be unity. Each move they made towards the smaller church was countered by a flight away until the differences seemed irreconcilable.

If you want to reflect further on this you may like to meditate on John 17, the prayer of Jesus before going to Gethsemane. He pleads that his followers will know both truth and unity.

Through the years of the church an emphasis on truth has led to constant disagreements and consequently many divisions. What would have happened if there had been an overemphasis on unity is historical guesswork but inevitably it would have led to a fuzziness about truth (although I realise in saying that that I am a man! If you are a woman you may want to comment about men in leadership).

As you meditate, think about all those families you know in which the father cannot agree with his grown-up sons and it is the mother who tries to be the reconciler. For everyone's health it might be better if the men tried to patch it up, whilst the mother recognised that no two people see things the same way.

THE PERSONAL STORIES END

We now come to the concluding episodes of the three stories we have been following. You might like to refresh you memory from Units 3, 5, 6 and 7. In this Unit we are thinking about action. Each of these people now relates the action they took. In one there is the beginning of the next cycle of reflection.

In the light of their reflection, these people have now chosen to act, and have done so courageously and meaningfully.

You may need for a moment to note the cost of their obedience and to thank God for their stories.

In which of these reflections is there the beginnings of the new cycle of reflection?

Alison

I moved into the new post with fear and trepidation, especially when my irascible new boss made it clear that to spend any part of a weekend at church was indeed a very stupid thing to do! Yet quite convinced that I was there for a purpose, and that the job was the right one for me.

Within a few months of taking the post, I received a phone call from my boss who was off sick, asking me to accompany her to hospital for an X-ray, as she was ill, with a severe chest infection. Both she and I knew the possible implications of her illness as she was a heavy smoker. I was appalled and amazed that she asked me to go with her, as my relationship with her had not been easy.

It shortly became evident that her illness was indeed serious, and after quickly taking early retirement she moved away from the area. However she asked me to visit her regularly, and over the next few months as she deteriorated, it was my privilege for God to use me to lead her into a very close relationship with God. The last time I visited her, it was obvious that the end was near, and with the agreement of her local vicar, she and I planned her funeral service, she chose the hymns, and indicated which prayers she would prefer to have. Her funeral was a sad, joyous occasion.

What a lesson I had learnt, by allowing God into my work life. He was able to use me in this situation, but more than that, of course, I became a changed person. I no longer needed my own power and authority in order to survive.

Now it is time for you to work again on the personal reflections you began in Unit 3. You are now to write about action based on the re-telling of the story in Unit 7. If you have information about the new cycle of reflection in the light of that action, write that also.

Try writing this down in 300 – 500 words, for at least one of your reflections.

Tony and Jayne

Jayne and I made the irrevocable decision to move. Early retirement was agreed by my employers, the house put on the market, and our sons informed.

Try as we might, we could not get a suitable house in the locality we wanted. 'Large garden with small retirement home attached' might have been a good description of what seemed appropriate. We continued to seek God's guidance about the new home. Eventually we began to discern that the new 'pasture' was to be radically different from the 'field' we were leaving. Maybe Jayne's homemaking was to be important in this new setting. Almost as soon as this was acknowledged a 'larger home with a smaller garden' was found, as was a buyer for our old home.

The retirement parties were held, and the removers did their work. I found it hard to settle to this new life. Not that I was idle. There was plenty to do but somehow there was still a sense of being uncertain about the long term. 'What am I here for?' I could be heard muttering. We went back to the image of the shepherd. It was pointed out that the shepherd moved the sheep for them to enjoy the new pasture. It might be that the purpose of the move was not that I did some major work for God but that God was giving us a place to delight in.

Our elder son was seemingly indifferent to the change. Manipulation continued. However, the move had given us both the means and resolve to make him take responsibility for himself, accepting that his failure was both possible and likely.

The image of the shepherd also came to the fore again when we began to notice that God was calling us to be shepherds. Taking our cue from Him we might be able to shepherd others -- calling to great change, acknowledging the weaknesses that made it difficult, and supporting and encouraging at every stage.

GLORIOUS!

When we are in the process of 'all change' there are some real glimpses of God's glory. The 'new' has delightful though unexpected facets that are really quite unimaginable whilst the 'old' is still operative. We are to be vigilant. The signs of God's touch are to be recognised, relished – and the cause of much thanksgiving.

Sarah

During the protracted and painful legal process and the long difficult months that followed, I was comforted and strengthened at different times by readings from Isaiah. By allowing God to travel with me through every step of the way I feel that I have honoured him and he has brought me through it all 'damaged but not destroyed'.

I refused to fight my husband in the secular way that the lawyers desired and would have found most lucrative. I still cringe from the memories of Jeremy in court cruelly dismantling me and my life, rubbishing all the precious times, just to procure a greater proportion of any financial settlement. Our family home had to be sold.

Where would I live? Could I afford to keep the car? Could I stay in the parish? Would I have to find a new job, church, friends? There was always one more decision round the corner. A flat, just big enough, was available at the eleventh hour. I have increased my work but despite that there is the prospect of long-term debt.

I have to learn how to be single again. It is a little like waking up after a long sleep, and finding the goal posts have shifted. Healthy new 'growth' is beginning, but it is slow and I feel no desire to hurry. I want it to be natural and right.

The positive side is that I now have a new freedom, personally and spiritually. I enjoy a greater responsibility within my own church who have supported me through the years, and I have become a Novice with the Third Order of St. Francis. I am learning to trust God and enjoy Him, and accept that He does have plans for me that will not be spoilt because of my weakness and difficulties.

The knowledge of His presence has given me the ability to pick up the threads of a new life.

THE WORLD STORIES END

We now come to the concluding episodes of the accounts of reflection in the wider world.

Note which results of these reflections seem positive and which seem negative.

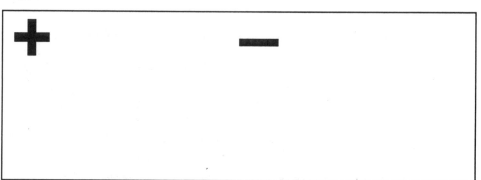

+	**—**

Martin's story

Martin was faced with the major task of presenting the plans to the company's board of directors. They noted the plans for slimming down the enterprise. As expected the discussion was most fierce when he argued that they had responsibilities and opportunities beyond simple profit.

As they talked about Martin's package of measures to alleviate the difficulties, they also began to recognise that such care might not just be a financial drain. A workforce that was respected might mean that the remaining people also felt respected. There was always the danger in a business that was slimming down that, instead of people being put on their toes to keep their jobs, resignation and hopelessness would set in on both sides of the factory gate. The results of a demoralised workforce would show themselves in the quality of the product and in absenteeism and sickness rates.

If respect was a factor on both sides of the factory gate, so too was optimism. If their customers felt that inevitably they would go out of business, then they would be likely to transfer their source of supply to competitors sooner rather than later. Wholesale closures could have a domino effect and do great damage to what remained of the business. If they could show that they were responding with optimism to the new economic outlook, they would keep friends.

Martin's package was accepted more or less. He could not stand in the way of economic change, but as a Christian he had shown that there were sound business arguments for acting in a way that was neither ruthless nor uncompassionate but nearer God's kingdom.

Martin's actions were not without cost. His health suffered greatly from the stress involved. But many families in their sadness at losing employment were unaware that they had much to be thankful for – a Christian man openly but quietly being 'for Christ' at the company head office.

JOYFUL DEATH

Martin's story reminds me of a deep truth from the hospice movement. They know that for some patients cure is not possible. Palliative care is undertaken in a spirit of joy rather than resignation. Respect, hope and relief of pain are very positive.

The village church story

The dire predictions proved reliable. The villagers vowed never to set foot inside a new church building. The lack of money was good reason not to think any further about it. The church authorities were not exactly brimming over with confidence. Plenty of the church members thought it a good idea but could not imagine the possibility. Some actively campaigned against it, for they knew where their power to stay cold yet cosy came from.

However it was not all negative. A building site was available right where the communities met. The borough council were impressed by the idea and would be sympathetic to a planning application.

The Church Council continued to pray. The breakthrough was a legacy, totally out of the blue, that gave a great start to a building fund. Money trickled in, mainly from the pensioners that made up the church. The church authorities found a source of some funds and it was able to go to the real planning stage.

Five long years after the initial suggestions, the new church was opened. There was wonder in many eyes and much talk of God's grace. The new location was a success and brought such reconciliation that the church was soon contemplating building an extension.

On the other hand the group of villagers who had opposed the building never set foot in it. Though they stayed away from the old church through apathy, they positively refused to go to the new.

Paul's story

Just after Christmas Paul flew with his squadron to the Gulf. They were immediately sent to the desert. There was a steep learning curve as they adapted from manoeuvres in the forests of Germany to the real war in the desert.

Now in charge of 400 people forming a communications centre, Paul was at the centre of decision making. They were also a prime target for opposing forces, and defence was a major responsibility of his.

There were some surprising elements. The chaplains had been posted to the field hospitals miles away from the action. That left him taking services each day in full view of the whole station. Eventually part of his job was taken on by others and he was free to spend more time with his troops. Knowing him to be a man of faith he had innumerable conversations about life and death, heaven and hell – questions that except for the threat of sudden death would never have surfaced. He found that his public stance also gave senior officers who shared his faith the opportunity to support him in his 'chaplaincy' work.

The invasion having been prevented, the coalition forces moved onto the offensive, and Paul played his part in the liberation of Kuwait. Having seen the injustices and atrocities that had been committed against the citizens of Kuwait he was in no doubt that the war had been justified.

On returning home there were some big issues for Paul to face. In galvanising himself for the conflict he had found himself learning to hate the enemy. He had to find ways of letting go the malevolence. He had to find ways he could forgive himself for this attitude, which he knew had been responsible for a greater level of aggression in him than he could feel comfortable with.

Now it is time for you to work again on your own reflections. You are to write about action based on the re-telling of the story in Unit 7. If you have information about a new cycle of reflection in the light of action, write that also.

Try writing this down in 300 – 500 words, for at least **one** of your world reflections.

WRAPPING IT UP

In this workbook I have tried to teach you a process. It is about discerning the touch of God in your life and in the realities of the world around you.

Behind the process

This process depends on some underlying truths:

♦ God is consistent. He is not capricious in His dealings with us or with the world. How He sees a particular situation today and what He does in it, will be paralleled in how He has previously viewed similar situations.

♦ You have the choice to stand with God in His work – and by doing so you are a significant catalyst for change. You can choose not to come to a better understanding of God's work and not to get involved. The outcome will then be different, for you and for those around you.

♦ The God we worship delights to reveal himself. He wants human beings to know Him and to know His ways. Mysterious though He is, He is not an impenetrable mystery. As you engage in the process of 'God Thoughts', He will be active to bring about your greater understanding.

♦ The understanding God offers us is not to boost our cleverness or to give us an inflated ego. It is to enable us to act in concern with Him. Perhaps it is when we try to understand for the wrong reasons that we find him impenetrable!

These truths are essential to your understanding of the process. Theological reflection is not a slick formula – it needs to be undergirded by this kind of understanding.

The five stages

You will remember that we have worked through the process using five stages:

> 1. The starting point, whether *experience* or *faith*
> 2. Identifying the most significant issues
> 3. Searching for the connections
> 4. Retelling the story
> 5. Moving into action

You will also remember that since the action changes the story, the cycle can begin all over again.

These are the essential stages in the process of theological reflection. Hold onto this basic framework, and your God thoughts will yield many fruitful insights into your life and the world around you.

REGISTERING FOR TUTORIAL SUPPORT?

If you would like the help and support of a tutor, please fill in the form below. We will put you in touch with your tutor as soon as possible. You may photocopy this form if you prefer.

I want to study **God Thoughts** with a tutor. Please register my name.

Name Address   Postcode   Telephone

I enclose a cheque for £60.00 to cover the cost of tuition.

Please use the space below to tell us about yourself: something about your background and why you are interested in doing this course. It will be useful to your tutor to have this information.

Send this form, with your remittance, to: St John's Extension Studies, Bramcote, Nottingham NG9 3RL. Telephone 0115 925 1117 for enquiries and credit card payments. You can fax this form on 0115 943 6438.

Referred by:

Certificate in Christian Studies

The Certificate in Christian Studies is a practical course in applied theology, designed to equip people in every local church for ministry and mission. It is equivalent to one year of full-time study, spread over several years on a part-time basis. As a distance learning course, it is accessible throughout the UK and abroad.

A course to rely on

The CCS was established in 1978. Our current courses draw on 25 years of experience – and it shows in the quality of our study materials, tutorial help, administration and other support. Well over 6,000 people have completed all or part of the programme.

A course of Christian development

For many different kinds of people, the CCS has been a dependable way of developing their Christian learning and discipleship.

- Many have continued to serve God where they are – giving leadership to house groups, children's and youth work, and other roles in the church.
- Others have deepened their faith and witness in the world, living out a more thoughtful Christianity in the complexities of today's society.
- Others again have been enabled to progress to further studies, sometimes for formal ministries in the church.

For students wanting a more rigorous programme of learning, the Certificate of Higher Education in Theology & Vocation is a flexible but robust course of Christian training, drawing on the strengths of both the College's residential training programme and Extension Studies' expertise in distance learning. It combines an introduction to biblical and theological studies with an exploration of Christian vocation,

CERTIFICATE in CHRISTIAN STUDIES

ST JOHN'S EXTENSION STUDIES

to help those who want to discover God's future for them through a better understanding of the Christian faith.

The course can form the first stage of a BA (Honours) but it is also a complete course in its own right, leading to the award of a Certificate in Higher Education validated by the Open University. Students who complete Certificate level distance learning can proceed either to the St John's mixed mode course for ordination training, or continue by distance learning to Diploma level. Successful students will later have the option of completing their theology degree through independent study and short visits to college.

A national course

The number of local courses on the Christian faith has mushroomed in recent years. Local resources are necessarily limited, and the experience of students on such courses varies a great deal. By centralising the development of resources and serving a much wider Christian public, the CCS has established itself as a training course of known quality, widely accepted in many church circles. This has also helped those who have subsequently moved from one part of the country to another.

For a detailed prospectus on the Certificate in Christian Studies and the Certificate in Theology & Vocation :

Phone: 0115 925 1117

Write: St John's Extension Studies, Bramcote, Nottingham NG9 3RL

Fax: 0115 943 6438

E-mail: ext.studies@stjohns-nottm.ac.uk

TWO OTHER WORKBOOKS FROM A SERIES OF 10 AVAILABLE FROM ST JOHN'S EXTENSION STUDIES

PRICE: £10.95 (POST FREE)
PHONE 0115 925 1117
FOR CREDIT CARD SALE

God is revealed to us in Scripture as a person, someone with whom we are invited to have a personal relationship. The Bible imagery is breathtaking, even shocking, if we pause to think about it. The Church is the bride of Christ. Relationships don't get more intimate than that.

Our relationship with God is like many of our close relationships in life. They are complicated; they have a history; they sometimes feel very intimate, sometimes not; they have their difficult moments. But most important of all, they matter. Each is a vital, life-giving 'connection' with another person. That's why we hang in there, even when things get tough.

But even good relationships need nourishing. Married couples sometimes go on a 'marriage enrichment weekend'. This is not for couples in crisis; it's for couples who want their relationship to work even better,

because they really value it. This workbook is a resource for a similar 'faith enrichment' experience. It is for any who really value their relationship with God.

- It will help you review your spiritual life, where your values come from, why you believe what you do – just as couples often review attitudes from their parental homes which they have carried over (often unthinkingly) into the marriage.

- It will help you choose what is good from your Christian past, and discard what is no longer helping you keep close to God.

- It will then help you discover new resources, new insights, that may draw you into a depth of relationship with God which you may so far have found elusive.

We say that some people have a 'calling'. God showed them that He wanted them to be a missionary, a minister, a monk, and God opened the way for them to do so. The calling was clear, the step that needed making was clear, and they took it. Now they have a vocation.

For every Christian for whom that is true, there are dozens for whom it isn't. It's not that they love God less. It's not that they are unwilling to make sacrifices in order to serve God. They may even have some sense that God is calling them – to something. It's just that the whole thing is not that clear.

This is hardly surprising. The issue of Christian calling has been poorly taught in our churches. The remarkable 'calls' of some great saints in Scripture and in the history of the Church have been held up as some kind of norm or ideal. Calling has also been seen in highly individual terms, dwarfing

the calling of the Church as a whole. And sadly, the idea of vocation has been attached to particular Christian roles which need funding – because this way people will feel it worthwhile to give money to support them.

God has purposes in this world. He calls each of us to become part of them. To do that, we need to understand those purposes, and see where we fit within them.

This workbook enables you to do that.
- It helps you understand the kind of life that God calls His people to live.
- It explores the place the Church has in working out God's kingdom purposes.
- It enables you to discover where you and your gifts fit in all this – including whether you might indeed become a missionary, a minister or a monk or nun.

It also helps you become fit for that purpose. Often we need to grow in

order to be the shape God needs for a particular role. If you are willing to do that, the testimony of God's people over many ages is that in pursuing God's call, with all its demands, you will find a new depth of Christian life and experience.